McDougal Littell

WORLD HISTORY

PATTERNS OF INTERACTION

In-Depth Resources: Unit 2

New Directions in Government and Society

McDougal Littell

A DIVISION OF HOUGHTON MIFFLIN COMPANY

Acknowledgments

CHAPTER 5

Excerpt from *The Odyssey of Homer*, translated by Richmond Lattimore. Copyright © 1965, 1967 by Richmond Lattimore. Copyright renewed. Reprinted by permission of HarperCollins Publishers, Inc.

Excerpt from *The Republic of Plato*, translated by Francis MacDonald Cornford. Published by Oxford University Press, London, 1941. Reprinted by permission of Oxford University Press.

CHAPTER 6

Excerpt from *The Gallic War and Other Writings by Julius Caesar*, translated by Moses Hadas. Copyright © 1957 by Random House, Inc. Reprinted by permission of Random House, Inc.

CHAPTER 7

"The Lion-Makers," from *The Panchatantra*, translated by Arthur W. Ryder. Copyright 1925 by The University of Chicago. Copyright renewed 1953 by Mary E. Ryder and Winifred Ryder. All rights reserved. Reprinted by permission of The University of Chicago Press.

Excerpt from *Pan Chao: Foremost Woman Scholar of China*, translated and edited by Nancy Lee Swann. Reprinted by permission of the Gest Oriental Library, Princeton University.

CHAPTER 8

Excerpt from "Periplus of the Erythaean Sea," from *Travellers in Ethiopia*, edited by Richard Pankhurst. Copyright © 1965 by Oxford University Press. Reproduced by permission of Oxford University Press.

Excerpt from "The Queen of Sheba and Her Only Son Menyelik," from *Kebra Negast,* translated by Sir Ernest A. Wallis Budge. Reprinted by permission of the copyright holders, University College, Oxford and Christ's College, Cambridge.

CHAPTER 9

"Ancient Puzzles and New Ones" by Lewis Lord, *U.S. News & World Report.* Copyright, February 24, 1997, U.S. News & World Report. Reprinted by permission.

Excerpt from *Mexico* by James A. Michener. Copyright © 1992 by James A. Michener. Reprinted by permission of Random House, Inc.

Excerpt from "Tales from a Peruvian Crypt" by Walter Alva and Christopher B. Donnan, *Natural History,* May 1994. Copyright © 1994 by the American Museum of Natural History. With permission from Natural History, May 1994.

ISBN 0-618-40912-2

Printed in the United States of America.

3 4 5 6 7 8 9 - VEI - 09 08 07 06 05 04

Unit 2 New Directions in Government and Society 2000 B.C.–A.D. 700

CHAPTER 5 Classical Greece, 2000 B.C.–300 B.C.

CHAPTER 6 Ancient Rome and Early Christianity, 500 B.C.–A.D. 500

CHAPTER ⑨ The Americas: A Separate World, 40,000 B.C.–A.D. 700

Name _____ Date _____

CHAPTER
5
Section 1

GUIDED READING *Cultures of the*
Mountains and the Sea

A. *Analyzing Causes and Recognizing Effects* As you read this section, make
notes in the chart to explain how each geographic characteristic or historical event
influenced the history and culture of early Greek civilization.

History and Culture	
1. Location "around" a sea	
2. Rugged mountains	
3. Little fertile farmland	
4. Moderate climate	
5. Mycenaean adaptation of Minoan culture	
6. The Trojan War	
7. The collapse of Mycenaean civilization	

B. *Determining Main Ideas* On the back of this paper, explain the significance of
myths and the epics of **Homer** in ancient Greek culture.

CHAPTER 5

GUIDED READING *Warring City-States*

Section 2

A. *Analyzing Causes and Recognizing Effects* As you read about the growth of Greek city-states, answer the questions about events in the time line. (Some dates are approximate.)

725 B.C.	**Sparta conquers Messenia.** →	1. How did Sparta treat the Messenians?
650 B.C.	**Spartans put down a revolt by Messenians.**	2. What type of society did Sparta create in response to the revolt?
621 B.C.	**Draco writes the first legal code.**	3. How did Athenians avoid major political upheavals?
594 B.C.	**Athenian aristocrats choose Solon to govern.**	4. What economic and political reforms did Solon initiate?
500 B.C.	**Cleisthenes introduces political reforms in Athens.**	5. What steps did Cleisthenes take to create a limited democracy in Athens?
490 B.C.	**Athenians defeat Persians in battle at Marathon.**	6. What advantages did the Greek soldiers have over the Persians?
479 B.C.	**Greeks defeat remaining Persian army.** →	7. What were the consequences of the Persian Wars?

B. *Determining Main Ideas* On the back of this paper, explain the relationship between the **polis** and **monarchy, aristocracy, oligarchy, tyrants,** and **democracy**.

Name _____ Date _____

CHAPTER
5
Section 3

GUIDED READING *Democracy and Greece's Golden Age*

A. *Summarizing* As you read this section, take notes to answer questions about Athens' golden age.

Pericles had three goals for Athens.

1. How did Pericles strengthen democracy?	2. What steps did Pericles take to strengthen the empire and glorify Athens?

The Greeks invented drama.

3. What themes were common in Greek tragedy?	4. What do the themes of Greek comedies suggest about the men and women of Athens?

Greek philosophers search for truth.

5. What was Plato's vision of the ideal society?	6. What is the philosophic legacy of Aristotle?

B. *Analyzing Causes and Recognizing Effects* On the back of this paper, briefly explain the causes and consequences of the **Peloponnesian War.**

Classical Greece 3

Name _____ Date _____

CHAPTER

5

Section 4

GUIDED READING *Alexander's Empire*

A. *Analyzing Causes and Recognizing Effects* As you read about the empire building of Alexander, note the goals and results of some of his actions.

Action(s)	Goal(s)	Result(s)
1. Led soldiers across Hellespont into Anatolia		
2. Launched surprise attack against Persians near Issus		
3. Rejected Darius' peace settlement of all lands west of Euphrates River		
4. Launched a phalanx attack followed by a cavalry charge at Gaugamela		
5. Led army into Indus Valley		

B. *Drawing Conclusions* On the back of this paper, explain how **Philip II** and **Demosthenes** are linked in the history of classical Greece.

Name _____   Date _____

GUIDED READING *The Spread of Hellenistic Culture*

_____

A. *Summarizing* As you read this section, fill in the diagram by listing the achievements of Hellenistic scholars and philosophers.

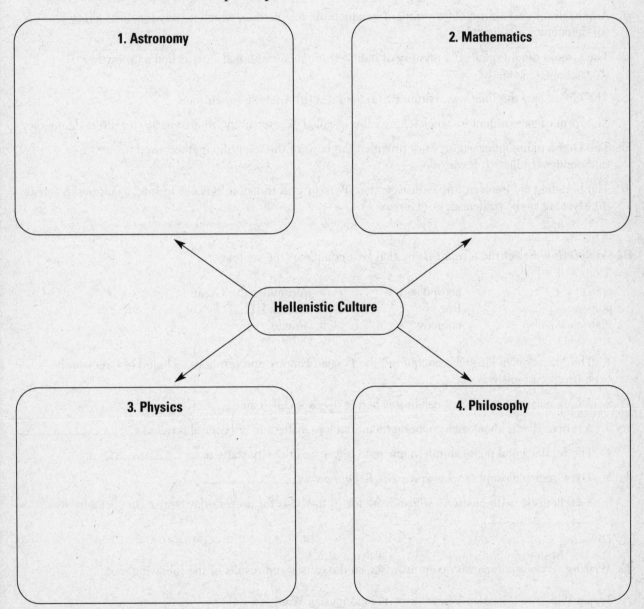

1. Astronomy

2. Mathematics

Hellenistic Culture

3. Physics

4. Philosophy

B. *Clarifying* Define **Hellenistic** and explain how **Alexandria** became a center of Hellenistic culture.

CHAPTER 5

BUILDING VOCABULARY *Classical Greece*

A. *Multiple Choice* Circle the letter before the term or name that best completes the sentence.

1. Athens developed a form of government in which the people rule, which is called (a) aristocracy (b) democracy (c) oligarchy.

2. The Greeks often explained a mystery of nature through a traditional story called a (a) myth (b) tragedy (c) comedy.

3. The Greek epic the *Iliad* was written by (a) Socrates (b) Aristotle (c) Homer.

4. The form of government in which a king rules is called (a) monarchy (b) aristocracy (c) direct democracy.

5. The Greek philosopher whose work provided the basis of the scientific method used today was (a) Socrates (b) Plato (c) Aristotle.

6. The blending of Greek culture with Egyptian, Persian, and Indian influences formed a culture known as (a) Mycenaean (b) Hellenistic (c) Dorian.

B. *Completion* Select the term or name that best completes the sentence.

epic	acropolis	Alexander the Great
polis	tragedy	Darius III
Plato	comedy	Euclid

1. The Macedonian king who conquered the Persian Empire and promoted a blend of Greek and Eastern customs was _____.

2. A long narrative poem that celebrates heroic deeds is called an _____.

3. A serious drama about such common themes as love, hate, war, or betrayal is called a _____.

4. The fundamental political unit in ancient Greece was the city-state, or _____.

5. The Greek philosopher who wrote *The Republic* was _____.

6. A Hellenistic mathematician whose work forms the basis for present-day courses in geometry was _____.

C. *Writing* Write a comparison-contrast essay on the causes and results of the following wars.

Trojan War   Persian Wars   Peloponnesian War

CHAPTER
5
Section 3

SKILLBUILDER PRACTICE *Analyzing Motives*

When you analyze motives, you examine the reasons why a person, group, or government took a particular action. These reasons can be rooted in the needs, emotions, experiences, or goals of the person or group. The passage below is from a funeral oration delivered by Pericles in honor of Athenian soldiers. As you read, keep in mind Pericles' goals for Athens—to strengthen Athenian democracy, to hold and strengthen the empire, and to glorify Athens. Then answer the questions that follow. (See Skillbuilder Handbook)

But before I praise the dead, I should like to point out by what principles of action we rose to power, and under what institutions and through what manner of life our empire became great. . . .

Our form of government does not enter into rivalry with the institutions of others. We do not copy our neighbors, but are an example to them.

It is true that we are called a democracy, for the administration is in the hands of the many and not of the few. . . .

And we have not forgotten to provide for our weary spirits many relaxations from toil. . . .

Because of the greatness of our city the fruits of the whole earth flow in upon us; so that we enjoy the goods of other countries as freely as our own.

Then, again, our military training is in many respects superior to that of our adversaries. . . . And in the matter of education, whereas they from early youth are always undergoing laborious exercises which are to make them brave, we live at ease, and yet are equally ready to face the perils which they face. . . . [W]e can be as brave as those who never allow themselves to rest; and thus too our city is equally admirable in peace and in war.

from Thucydides, *History of the Peloponnesian War,* translated by Benjamin Jowett.

1. The purpose of Pericles' speech was to honor those who had died in the early campaigns of the Peloponnesian War. What might have been his motives in speaking first of how Athens became a great empire?

_____

_____

2. a. Why do you think Pericles referred to the Spartans without once mentioning them by name?

_____

_____

  b. What probably were Pericles' motives in comparing Athens and Sparta? _____

_____

3. How do you think Pericles' goals for Athens affected the content and tone of his funeral oration?

_____

_____

Name _____ Date _____

GEOGRAPHY APPLICATION: HUMAN–ENVIRONMENT INTERACTION

The Peloponnesian War

Directions: Read the paragraphs below and study the map carefully. Then answer the questions that follow.

The two Greek city-states of Sparta and Athens maintained an uneasy existence in the fifth century B.C. Spartan discipline, militarism, and aristocratic rule were in direct opposition to creative, vibrant, and democratic Athens.

The immediate cause of the Peloponnesian War was Athenian expansion onto the island of Corcyra in 431 B.C., which threatened the Spartan ally of Corinth. The coastal city of Athens, without a strong army, used its navy to raid the Spartan coast, supply the city of Athens, and maintain contact with its allies. On the other hand, the landlocked Spartans ravaged the countryside with their army, forcing the Athenians to hide within their city walls. A truce was finally arranged in 421 B.C. after ten indecisive years. However, Athens broke the peace in 415 B.C. with a poorly planned attack on Syracuse, a Spartan ally located on the island of Sicily. The invasion failed miserably, and the Spartans, with their new ally of Persia, eventually forced the surrender of Athens in 404 B.C. The entire Greek world, though, felt the loss as the Greek city-states began a continuous period of decline.

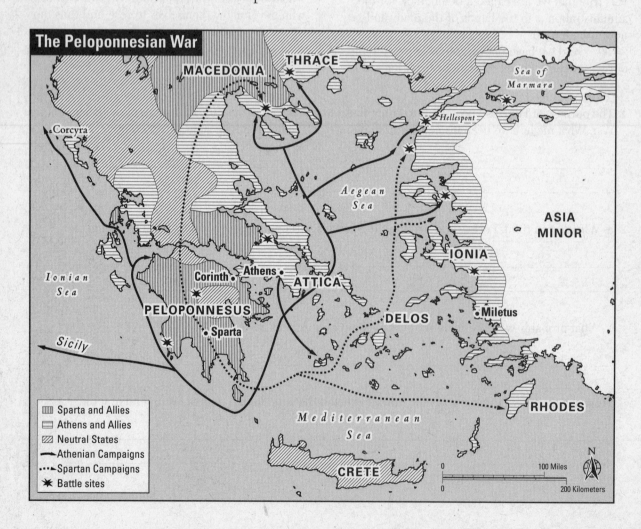

The Peloponnesian War

Legend:
- Sparta and Allies
- Athens and Allies
- Neutral States
- Athenian Campaigns
- Spartan Campaigns
- ✳ Battle sites

Interpreting Text and Visuals

1. Name the three bodies of water that form the backdrop for the Spartan and Athenian campaigns.

_____

_____

2. Compare the positioning of Athens and its allies to that of Sparta and its allies. _____

_____

_____

3. Which city-state seemed to have the geographical advantage? Why? _____

_____

_____

4. Does Athens or Sparta have more geographic area on the map? _____

5. Which city-state appears to control the Greek peninsula? _____

_____

6. Why was this war called the Peloponnesian War? _____

_____

7. How do the arrows indicating Athenian campaigns reflect their overall strategy for the war?

_____

_____

_____

_____

_____

_____

_____

_____

PRIMARY SOURCE *from* The History of Herodotus

Section 2

Herodotus, who is often regarded as the first historian, was a Greek scholar who lived in the fifth century B.C. In this passage he describes the battle of Marathon, waged between the Persians (whom Herodotus sometimes refers to as Medes) and the Greeks in 490 B.C. during the Persian Wars. Miltiades, one of ten Greek generals, has persuaded the other generals to fight the Persians at once, although some generals wanted to avoid battle when the Persians so greatly outnumbered the Greeks. As you read this excerpt, think about why the outnumbered Greeks defeated the Persians.

111. Then at length, when his [Miltiades'] own turn was come, the Athenian battle was set in array, and this was the order of it. Callimachus the Polemarch led the right wing; for it was at that time a rule with the Athenians to give the right wing to the Polemarch. After this followed the tribes, according as they were numbered, in an unbroken line; while last of all came the Platæans, forming the left wing. And ever since that day it has been a custom with the Athenians, in the sacrifices and assemblies held each fifth year at Athens, for the Athenian herald to implore the blessing of the gods on the Platæans conjointly with the Athenians. Now, as they marshalled [arranged in battle order] the host upon the field of Marathon, in order that the Athenian front might be of equal length with the Median, the ranks of the centre were diminished, and it became the weakest part of the line, while the wings were both made strong with depth of many ranks.

112. So when the battle was set in array, and the victims showed themselves favourable, instantly the Athenians, so soon as they were let go, charged the barbarians at a run. Now the distance between the two armies was little short of eight furlongs [less than one mile]. The Persians, therefore, when they saw the Greeks coming on at speed, made ready to receive them, although it seemed to them that the Athenians were bereft of their senses, and bent upon their own destruction; for they saw a mere handful of men coming on at a run without either horsemen or archers. Such was the opinion of the barbarians; but the Athenians in close array fell upon them, and fought in a manner worthy of being recorded. They were the first of the Greeks, so far as I know, who introduced the custom of charging the enemy at a run, and they were likewise the first who dared to look upon the Median garb, and to face men clad in that fashion. Until this time the very name of the Medes had been a

terror to the Greeks to hear.

113. The two armies fought together on the plain of Marathon for a length of time; and in the mid battle, where the Persians themselves and the Sacæ had their place, the barbarians were victorious, and broke and pursued the Greeks into the inner country; but on the two wings the Athenians and the Platæans defeated the enemy. Having so done, they suffered the routed [defeated] barbarians to fly at their ease, and joining the two wings in one, fell upon those who had broken their own centre, and fought and conquered them. These likewise fled, and now the Athenians hung upon the runaways and cut them down, chasing them all the way to the shore, on reaching which they laid hold of the ships and called aloud for fire.

114. It was in the struggle here that Callimachus the Polemarch, after greatly distinguishing himself, lost his life; Stesilaüs too, the son of Thrasilaüs, one of the generals, was slain; and Cynægirus, the son of Euphorion, having seized on a vessel of the enemy's by the ornament at the stern, had his hand cut off by the blow of an axe, and so perished; as likewise did many other Athenians of note and name.

from George Rawlinson, trans., *The History of Herodotus* (Chicago: Encyclopædia Britannica, 1952), 207–208.

Discussion Questions

1. *Making Inferences* Who joined the Athenians to fight the Persians at the battle of Marathon?
2. *Clarifying* According to this account, what famous Greeks died in the battle?
3. *Drawing Conclusions* Why do you think the Greeks defeated the Persians in this battle?

Name _____   Date _____

PRIMARY SOURCE # Plague in Athens
by Thucydides

Section 3   *Thucydides, an Athenian historian, fought in the Peloponnesian War between Athens and Sparta. After being exiled by the Athenians following a particularly costly defeat, Thucydides spent the next 20 years writing a history of the war. This excerpt from his* History *describes an outbreak of an unidentified disease that caused a deadly plague in Athens in 430 B.C., at the height of the war.*

The disease began, it is said, in Ethiopia beyond Egypt, and then descended into Egypt and Libya and spread over the greater part of the King's territory. Then it suddenly fell upon the city of Athens, and attacked first the inhabitants of the Peiraeus . . . I shall describe its actual course, explaining the symptoms, from the study of which a person should be best able, having knowledge of it beforehand, to recognize it if it should ever break out again. For I had the disease myself and saw others sick of it.

That year, as was agreed by all, happened to be unusually free from disease so far as regards the other maladies; but if anyone was already ill of any disease all terminated in this. In other cases from no obvious cause, but suddenly and while in good health, men were seized first with intense heat of the head, and redness and inflammation of the eyes, and the parts inside the mouth, both the throat and the tongue, immediately became blood-red and exhaled an unnatural and fetid breath. In the next stage sneezing and hoarseness came on, and in a short time the disorder descended to the chest, attended by severe coughing. And when it settled in the stomach, that was upset, and vomits of bile of every kind named by physicians ensued, these also attended by great distress; and in most cases ineffectual retching followed producing violent convulsions, which sometimes abated [lessened] directly, sometimes not until long afterwards. . . . They were also beset by restlessness and sleeplessness which never abated. And the body was not wasted while the disease was at its height, but resisted surprisingly the ravages of the disease, so that when the patients died, as most of them did on the seventh or ninth day from the internal heat, they still had some strength left; or, if they passed the crisis, the disease went down into the bowels, producing there a violent ulceration, and at the same time an acute diarrhoea set in, so that in this

later stage most of them perished through weakness caused by it. . . . And the most dreadful thing about the whole malady was not only the despondency of the victims, when they once became aware that they were sick, for their minds straightway yielded to despair and they gave themselves up for lost instead of resisting, but also the fact that they became infected by nursing one another and died like sheep. . . . Bodies of dying men lay one upon another, and half-dead people rolled about in the streets and, in their longing for water, near all the fountains. The temples, too, in which they had quartered themselves were full of the corpses of those who had died in them; for the calamity which weighed upon them was so overpowering that men, not knowing what was to become of them, became careless of all law, sacred as well as profane. . . . And many resorted to shameless modes of burial because so many members of their households had already died that they lacked the proper funeral materials. Resorting to other people's pyres, some, anticipating those who had raised them, would put on their own dead and kindle the fire; others would throw the body they were carrying upon one which was already burning and go away.

from C.F. Smith, trans., *History* by Thucydides (Loeb, 1919). Reprinted in John Carey, ed., *Eyewitness to History* (New York: Avon, 1987), 1–2.

Activity Options

1. *Summarizing* Imagine that you have been asked to prepare a health bulletin to inform Athenians about this deadly disease. List possible symptoms in the order in which they occur.
2. *Making Generalizations* Invite a physician or another health professional in your community to speak to the class about possible causes of this disease and how Athenians might have prevented its spread.

PRIMARY SOURCE *from* The Republic
by Plato

Plato, a Greek philosopher and writer, lived in Athens during its golden age. Much of his work takes the form of a dialogue between two or more people. In this excerpt from Plato's most famous work, The Republic, *the Greek philosopher Socrates and Plato's older brother Glaucon hold a conversation about the ideal statesman. According to Plato, why should philosophers run the government?*

The Philosopher's Fitness to Rule

So at last, Glaucon, after this long and weary way, we have come to see who are the philosophers and who are not.

I doubt if the way could have been shortened.

Apparently not. I think, however, that we might have gained a still clearer view, if this had been the only topic to be discussed; but there are so many others awaiting us, if we mean to discover in what ways the just life is better than the unjust.

Which are we to take up now?

Surely the one that follows next in order. Since the philosophers are those who can apprehend the eternal and unchanging, while those who cannot do so, but are lost in the mazes of multiplicity and change, are not philosophers, which of the two ought to be in control of a state?

I wonder what would be a reasonable solution.

To establish as Guardians whichever of the two appear competent to guard the laws and ways of life in society.

True.

Well, there can be no question whether a guardian who is to keep watch over anything needs to be keen-sighted or blind. And is not blindness precisely the condition of men who are entirely cut off from knowledge of any reality, and have in their soul no clear pattern of perfect truth, which they might study in every detail and constantly refer to, as a painter looks at his model, before they proceed to embody notions of justice, honour, and goodness in earthly institutions or, in their character of Guardians, to preserve such institutions as already exist?

Certainly such a condition is very like blindness.

Shall we, then, make such as these our Guardians in preference to men who, besides their knowledge of realities, are in no way inferior to them in experience and in every excellence of character?

It would be absurd not to choose the philosophers, whose knowledge is perhaps their greatest point of superiority, provided they do not lack those other qualifications.

What we have to explain, then, is how those qualifications can be combined in the same persons with philosophy.

Certainly.

The first thing, as we said at the outset, is to get a clear view of their inborn disposition. When we are satisfied on that head, I think we shall agree that such a combination of qualities is possible and that we need look no further for men fit to be in control of a commonwealth. One trait of the philosophic nature we may take as already granted: a constant passion for any knowledge that will reveal to them something of that reality which endures for ever and is not always passing into and out of existence. And, we may add, their desire is to know the whole of that reality; they will not willingly renounce any part of it as relatively small and insignificant, as we said before when we compared them to the lover and to the man who covets honour.

True.

Is there not another trait which the nature we are seeking cannot fail to possess—truthfulness, a love of truth and a hatred of falsehood that will not tolerate untruth in any form?

Yes, it is natural to expect that.

It is not merely natural, but entirely necessary that an instinctive passion for any object should extend to all that is closely akin to it; and there is nothing more closely akin to wisdom than truth. So the same nature cannot love wisdom and falsehood; the genuine lover of knowledge cannot fail, from his youth up, to strive after the whole of truth.

I perfectly agree.

Now we surely know that when a man's desires set strongly in one direction, in every other channel they flow more feebly, like a stream diverted into another bed. So when the current has set towards knowledge and all that goes with it, desire will abandon those pleasures of which the body is the instrument and be concerned only with the pleasure which the soul enjoys independently—if, that is to say, the love of wisdom is more than a mere pretence. Accordingly, such a one will be temperate and no lover of money; for he will be the last person to care about the things for the sake of which money is eagerly sought and lavishly spent.

That is true.

Again, in seeking to distinguish the philosophic nature, you must not overlook the least touch of meanness. Nothing could be more contrary than pettiness to a mind constantly bent on grasping the whole of things, both divine and human.

Quite true.

And do you suppose that one who is so high-minded and whose thought can contemplate all time and all existence will count this life of man a matter of much concern?

No, he could not.

So for such a man death will have no terrors.

None.

A mean and cowardly nature, then, can have no part in the genuine pursuit of wisdom.

I think not.

And if a man is temperate and free from the love of money, meanness, pretentiousness, and cowardice, he will not be hard to deal with or dishonest. So, as another indication of the philosophic temper, you will observe whether, from youth up, he is fair-minded, gentle, and sociable.

Certainly.

Also you will not fail to notice whether he is quick or slow to learn. No one can be expected to take a reasonable delight in a task in which much painful effort makes little headway. And if he cannot retain what he learns, his forgetfulness will leave no room in his head for knowledge; and so, having all his toil for nothing, he can only end by hating himself as well as his fruitless occupation. We must not, then, count a forgetful mind as competent to pursue wisdom; we must require a good memory.

By all means.

Further, there is in some natures a crudity and awkwardness that can only tend to a lack of measure and proportion; and there is a close affinity [attraction or kinship] between proportion and truth. Hence, besides our other requirements, we shall look for a mind endowed with measure and grace, which will be instinctively drawn to see every reality in its true light.

Yes.

Well then, now that we have enumerated the qualities of a mind destined to take its full part in the apprehension of reality, have you any doubt about their being indispensable and all necessarily going together?

None whatever.

Then have you any fault to find with a pursuit which none can worthily follow who is not by nature quick to learn and to remember, magnanimous [unselfish] and gracious, the friend and kinsman of truth, justice, courage, temperance?

No. . . .

Well then, when time and education have brought such characters as these to maturity, would you entrust the care of your commonwealth to anyone else?

from Francis Cornford, trans., *The Republic of Plato* (London: Oxford University Press, 1974), 189–192.

Activity Options

1. ***Determining Main Ideas*** With a partner, role-play a conversation between Socrates and Glaucon about why philosophers should control the government.

2. ***Drawing Conclusions*** List qualities of an ideal statesman according to this excerpt. Then decide whether Pericles fits the description of an ideal ruler based on what you have read about him.

3. ***Analyzing Issues*** Discuss with your classmates which political leaders in countries around the world today best exemplify Plato's ideal ruler.

CHAPTER
5

Section 3

PRIMARY SOURCE *from* Politics
by Aristotle

The Greek philosopher Aristotle (384–322 B.C.) spent 20 years at Plato's Academy. He eventually started his own school and tutored Alexander until his royal student became the king of Macedonia. Aristotle wrote influential books on many different topics, including biology, rhetoric, poetry, and politics. As you read this passage from Book IV of Aristotle's Politics, *think about how he uses logic to arrive at definitions of two principal forms of government that existed in ancient Greece.*

One should not regard democracy, in the way some are now accustomed to do, as being simply where the multitude is in control (for, in fact, both in oligarchies and everywhere else, the greater part is in control), nor should one regard oligarchy as being where few have control over the regime. For if the whole number were 1,300, and 1,000 of these were rich but gave no share in rule to the 300 who, though free and similar in other respects, were poor, no one would say that they were running a democracy. Likewise too, if the poor were few but stronger than the well-off, who were more numerous, no one would call such a regime an oligarchy if the others, though wealthy, had no share in the honors. It should, then, rather be said that popular rule is when the free are in control and oligarchy is when the rich are; but it happens that the first are many and the second few, since many are free and few are rich. For otherwise there would be an oligarchy if offices were distributed according to size, as some say is the case in Ethiopia, or according to beauty, because the beautiful and the tall are few in number.

Yet it is not even enough to distinguish these regimes by these criteria alone. Rather, since there are several parts to the populace and to oligarchy, it is necessary to grasp further that neither would there be popular rule if the free who were few were ruling over those who were a majority and not free (as, for example, in Apollonia on the Ionian Gulf and in Thera, for in each of these cities the honors belonged to those who, though few among many, were superior in good birth and had got first possession of the colonies), nor would there be popular rule if the rich were superior in numbers (as, for example, in Colophon long ago, for there the majority had acquired much substance before the war against the Lydians). But it is democracy when the free and needy who are the majority have control of rule, and it is oligarchy when the rich and better born who are few have control.

from The Politics of Aristotle, Peter L. Phillips Simpson, trans. (Chapel Hill, North Carolina: The University of North Carolina Press: 1997), 175–176.

Discussion Questions

1. *Summarizing* Greek city-states adopted several different forms of government—monarchy, aristocracy, oligarchy, and direct democracy. Which two forms does Aristotle discuss in this passage?
2. *Clarifying* What two criteria did Aristotle use to describe the difference between these two forms of government?
3. *Drawing Conclusions* Which definition best describes the form of government that exists in the United States today? Explain your answer.

CHAPTER
5

Section 1

LITERATURE SELECTION *from Odyssey*
by Homer

*The Odyssey, the second of Homer's epics, tells the story of Odysseus and his
ten-year journey home from the Trojan War after taking part in a ten-year siege
of Troy by the Greeks. In this excerpt, Odysseus, disguised as a beggar, is reunit-
ed with his wife Penelope after killing all of his rivals who wanted to marry her.
To the annoyance of their son Telemachus, Penelope refuses to believe that
Odysseus has returned. As you read, think about how Penelope is finally persuaded of her husband's identity.*

Penelope spoke, and came down from the chamber, her heart pondering
much, whether to keep away and question her dear husband,
or to go up to him and kiss his head, taking his hands.
But then, when she came in and stepped over the stone threshold,
5   she sat across from him in the firelight, facing Odysseus,
by the opposite wall, while he was seated by the tall pillar,
looking downward, and waiting to find out if his majestic
wife would have anything to say to him, now that she saw him.
She sat a long time in silence, and her heart was wondering.
10   Sometimes she would look at him, with her eyes full upon him,
and again would fail to know him in the foul clothing he wore.
Telemachos spoke to her and called her by name and scolded her:
"My mother, my harsh mother with the hard heart inside you,
why do you withdraw so from my father, and do not
15   sit beside him and ask him questions and find out about him?
No other woman, with spirit as stubborn as yours, would keep back
as you are doing from her husband who, after much suffering,
came at last in the twentieth year back to his own country.
But always you have a heart that is harder than stone within you."
20   Circumspect [wise; careful] Penelope said to him in answer:
"My child, the spirit that is in me is full of wonderment,
and I cannot find anything to say to him, nor question him,
nor look him straight in the face. But if he is truly Odysseus,
and he has come home, then we shall find other ways, and better,
25   to recognize each other, for we have signs that we know of
between the two of us only, but they are secret from others."
So she spoke, and much-enduring noble Odysseus
smiled, and presently spoke in winged words to Telemachos:
"Telemachos, leave your mother to examine me in the palace
30   as she will, and presently she will understand better;
but now that I am dirty and wear foul clothing upon me,
she dislikes me for that, and says I am not her husband.
But let us make our plans how all will come out best for us.
For when one has killed only one man in a community,
35   and then there are not many avengers to follow, even
so, he flees into exile, leaving kinsmen and country.
But we have killed what held the city together, the finest
young men in Ithaka. It is what I would have you consider."
Then the thoughtful Telemachos said to him in answer:

40   "You must look to this yourself, dear father; for they say
       you have the best mind among men for craft, and there is
       no other man among mortal men who can contend with you.
       We shall follow you eagerly; I think that we shall not
       come short in warcraft, in so far as the strength stays with us."

45   Then resourceful Odysseus spoke in turn and answered him:
       "So I will tell you the way of it, how it seems best to me.
       First, all go and wash, and put your tunics upon you,
       and tell the women in the palace to choose out their clothing.
       Then let the inspired singer take his clear-sounding lyre,

50   and give us the lead for festive dance, so that anyone
       who is outside, some one of the neighbors, or a person going
       along the street, who hears us, will think we are having a wedding.
       Let no rumor go abroad in the town that the suitors
       have been murdered, until such time as we can make our way

55   out to our estate with its many trees, and once there
       see what profitable plan the Olympian shows us."
       So he spoke, and they listened well to him and obeyed him.
       First they went and washed, and put their tunics upon them,
       and the women arrayed themselves in their finery, while the inspired

60   singer took up his hollowed lyre and stirred up within them
       the impulse for the sweetness of song and the stately dancing.
       Now the great house resounded aloud to the thud of their footsteps,
       as the men celebrated there, and fair-girdled women;
       and thus would a person speak outside the house who heard them:

65   "Surely now someone has married our much-sought-after
       queen; hard-hearted, she had no patience to keep the great house
       for her own wedded lord to the end, till he came back to her."
       So would a person speak, but they did not know what had happened.
       Now the housekeeper Eurynome bathed great-hearted

70   Odysseus in his own house, and anointed him with olive oil,
       and threw a beautiful mantle and a tunic about him;
       and over his head Athene suffused [spread over] great beauty, to make him
       taller to behold and thicker, and on his head she arranged
       the curling locks that hung down like hyacinthine petals.

75   And as when a master craftsman overlays gold on silver,
       and he is one who was taught by Hephaistos [Greek god of fire] and Pallas Athene
       in art complete, and grace is on every work he finishes;
       so Athene gilded with grace his head and his shoulders.
       Then, looking like an immortal, he strode forth from the bath,

80   and came back then and sat on the chair from which he had risen,
       opposite his wife, and now he spoke to her, saying:
       "You are so strange. The gods, who have their homes on Olympos,
       have made your heart more stubborn than for the rest of womankind.
       No other woman, with spirit as stubborn as yours, would keep back

85   as you are doing from her husband who, after much suffering,
       came at last in the twentieth year back to his own country.
       Come then, nurse, make me up a bed, so that I can use it
       here; for this woman has a heart of iron within her."
       Circumspect Penelope said to him in answer:

90   "You are so strange. I am not being proud, nor indifferent,

95

nor puzzled beyond need, but I know very well what you looked like
when you went in the ship with the sweeping oars, from Ithaka.
Come then, Eurykleia, and make up a firm bed for him
outside the well-fashioned chamber: that very bed that he himself
built. Put the firm bed here outside for him, and cover it
over with fleeces and blankets, and with shining coverlets."
So she spoke to her husband, trying him out, but Odysseus
spoke in anger to his virtuous-minded lady:
"What you have said, dear lady, has hurt my heart deeply. What man

100

has put my bed in another place? But it would be difficult
for even a very expert one, unless a god, coming
to help in person, were easily to change its position.
But there is no mortal man alive, no strong man, who lightly
could move the weight elsewhere. There is one particular feature

105

in the bed's construction. I myself, no other man, made it.
There was the bole of an olive tree with long leaves growing
strongly in the courtyard, and it was thick, like a column.
I laid down my chamber around this, and built it, until I
finished it, with close-set stones, and roofed it well over,

110

and added the compacted doors, fitting closely together.
Then I cut away the foliage of the long-leaved olive,
and trimmed the trunk from the roots up, planing it with a brazen
adze [axe-like tool], well and expertly, and trued it straight to a chalkline,
making a bed post of it, and bored all holes with an auger.

115

I began with this and built my bed, until it was finished,
and decorated it with gold and silver and ivory.
Then I lashed it with thongs of oxhide, dyed bright with purple.
There is its character, as I tell you; but I do not know now,
dear lady, whether my bed is still in place, or if some man

120

has cut underneath the stump of the olive, and moved it elsewhere."
So he spoke, and her knees and the heart within her went slack
as she recognized the clear proofs that Odysseus had given;
but then she burst into tears and ran straight to him, throwing
her arms around the neck of Odysseus, and kissed his head, saying:

125

"Do not be angry with me, Odysseus, since, beyond other men,
you have the most understanding. The gods granted us misery,
in jealousy over the thought that we two, always together,
should enjoy our youth, and then come to the threshold of old age.
Then do not now be angry with me nor blame me, because

130

I did not greet you, as I do now, at first when I saw you.
For always the spirit deep in my very heart was fearful
that some one of mortal men would come my way and deceive me
with words. For there are many who scheme for wicked advantage.

from Richmond Lattimore, trans., *The Iliad and the Odyssey of
Homer*. Reprinted in *Great Books of the Western World*
(Chicago: Encyclopædia Britannica, 1993), 524–528.

Discussion Questions

1. *Recognizing Effects* How does Penelope respond before she is sure that Odysseus is her husband?

2. *Clarifying* What proof does Odysseus give that he is Penelope's husband?

3. *Drawing Conclusions* Based on your reading of this excerpt, what kind of person do you think Penelope is?

CHAPTER
5

Section 3

HISTORYMAKERS Sophocles
Author of the Human Drama

"Many are the wonders of the world, but none is more wonderful than man."
—*Sophocles*, Antigone

The great playwright Sophocles was born just before the Greek city-states faced the challenge of the Persian invasions. He lived through the golden age of Athens, when that city gave birth to a flowering of art, architecture, literature, and philosophy. The plays he wrote—only a few of which survive—put a new stamp on theater and influenced drama in the Western world for centuries.

Sophocles was born to a successful manufacturer of weapons in the town of Colonus, near Athens. When Sophocles was six years old, the Persians invaded Greece but met defeat in the famous Battle of Marathon. Just ten years later, the Greeks won another great victory when they destroyed the Persian fleet at Salamis. The young Sophocles led the chorus that sang a song of victory to mark this triumph.

By age 28, Sophocles had written at least one play, which he entered in an annual drama competition against Aeschylus. That playwright was almost 30 years older than Sophocles and his reputation was already established. Nevertheless, the judges found the play of Sophocles superior, and he won first prize. It was not the last time he would be honored in this way. Throughout his life, he won 18 first prizes and many second prizes, but never anything lower.

Sophocles played an active role in Athenian life. He was a close friend of the politician Pericles, the philosopher Socrates, and the historian Herodotus. He took part in the political life of Athens, serving once as treasurer and twice as a general. He also acted as a priest to one god and founded a shrine to another god. While these activities contributed to the civic life of Athens, they are not Sophocles' main claim to fame.

His major achievement was the writing of about 125 tragic plays. Unfortunately, only seven still survive in complete form. It is from those plays, the few fragments that survived, and the comments of his contemporaries that Sophocles is known as one of the world's major dramatists. His most well-known works are the plays *Antigone, Oedipus Rex, Electra,* and *Oedipus at Colonus. Antigone* and *Electra* are especially notable as the first plays to portray heroic women.

Before Sophocles, Greek theater was dominated by the work of Aeschylus. Plays were built around a chorus that commented on the action, which was dramatized by two characters at a time. The characters and members of the chorus all wore masks, and the Greek gods played major roles.

Sophocles began working in this style but eventually pointed the theater in new directions. He made the masks more expressive, enhancing the effect of his productions. He also added painted scenery to provide a more interesting setting for the action. Most important, he introduced a third character to the plays. This step allowed him to explore more complex human interactions.

That change went to the heart of Sophocles' drama. He was the founder of theater that explored the human condition. The gods play a role in his works, but not prominently. The action arises directly from the nature of the human characters. Sophocles' writing shows a person in crisis—often a crisis that arises directly from that person's identity. His characters suffer great pain as they wrestle with difficult questions of life: What is fate? What is justice? Each major character, though, must face personal responsibility for his or her actions. By watching them confront this crisis, the audience learns something essential about what it is to be a human being.

Questions

1. **Determining Main Ideas** How does the quotation from Sophocles at the top of the page relate to his approach to drama?
2. **Making Inferences** Sophocles was active in many aspects of Athenian life. What does that suggest about the Athenian view of citizenship?
3. **Drawing Conclusions** How did the changes that Sophocles made to theatrical practice add to the impact of his plays?

CHAPTER
5
Section 5

HISTORYMAKERS Archimedes
Genius of Legend, Genius in Fact

"Give me a place to stand on, and I can move the earth."—Archimedes explaining the use of levers and pulleys

Thinker and creative genius, the Greek mathematician Archimedes was famous in the ancient world for his inventions. He created devices used in peace and weapons used in war. He also did some important work that advanced mathematics. Many colorful legends arose about him—and many of them can be dismissed. Yet they cannot detract from his numerous accomplishments.

Archimedes's interest in science and mathematics should not be surprising. His father was an astronomer, which at the time was seen as a branch of mathematics. Archimedes was born around 287 B.C. in Syracuse, Sicily, a Greek colony. He studied for a while in Alexandria at the school founded by Euclid, another great Greek mathematician. Archimedes lived the rest of his life in Syracuse. In mathematics Archimedes explored many different ideas. For example, he tried to find the volume or area of a variety of geometric shapes, such as circles, cones, spheres, and cylinders. In this work, he used ratios to find the area of these figures. Archimedes often performed tasks on behalf of Hieron, the king of Syracuse. One story says that the king gave a goldsmith a quantity of gold and told him to make a crown. When it was finished, the king suspected that the goldsmith had placed silver inside, making the crown less valuable. The king asked Archimedes to find out if that were true. The mathematician used logic to discover the principle that explains the forces that keep a solid body afloat in water. With that knowledge, he could test the crown by comparing its weight in water against the weight of the correct quantity of gold. According to the story, Archimedes hit upon this idea one day as he rested in a bath. *"Eureka!"* (I have discovered it!), he yelled as he ran into the street—still naked from his bath.

While the details of this story are doubtful, there are several inventions of Archimedes that establish his brilliance. While in Egypt, he invented a device called the Archimedes screw. Because it could lift water to higher levels, the screw was useful for irrigating farmland. He also discovered the lever and the pulley, which could be used to move heavy objects. This invention prompted his statement that he could move the world. Finally, he designed and built a planetarium that showed the movement of the sun, the moon, and the five known planets. According to one account, the machine worked so well that it showed eclipses of the sun and moon. Among his most spectacular inventions were machines used for war. An ancient historian described what happened when the Romans attacked Syracuse:

> Archimedes began to work his engines and hurled against the land forces all sorts of missiles and huge masses of stones, which . . . knocked down in heaps those who stood in the way and threw the ranks in disorder . . . [He also used machines against ships.] Often there was the fearful sight of a ship lifted out of the sea into mid-air and whirled about as it hung there, until the men had been thrown out. . . .

Nevertheless, the Romans eventually captured Syracuse. The Roman general ordered his men to spare the people of the city. For some reason, that order was ignored with Archimedes. Upon finding him, a Roman soldier told him that he was to go see the Roman general. However, Archimedes delayed until he could finish working on a mathematical problem. The soldier, angry at him for disobeying, killed him. While the details are obscured by legend, the result is undisputed. The general ". . . turned away from the slayer as from a polluted person, and sought out the relatives of Archimedes to do them honor."

Questions

1. **Distinguishing Fact from Opinion** How can historians examine sources to separate legend from fact?

2. **Drawing Conclusions** Which of Archimedes' inventions do you think was the most significant? Explain.

3. **Making Inferences** Why do you think the Roman general reacted as he did to Archimedes' death?

Name _____ Date _____

CHAPTER 5
Section 3

Ideas of Government in Greece and China

THEMATIC CONNECTION:
POWER AND AUTHORITY

*In ancient Greece, city-states adopted several different forms of government,
including monarchy, aristocracy, oligarchy, tyranny, and democracy. In Chapter 4,
you learned about the conflicting ideas of Confucius and the Legalists about the
best way to govern. To increase your understanding of these varied ideas about
government, answer the following questions.*

1. The Legalists of ancient China thought that a single strong ruler should maintain
   harmony in the state by using generous rewards and harsh punishments.

   a. Which of the Greek forms of government is most like the Legalist ideal? Why? _____
   _____

   b. What might the Legalists have liked about the system of government in Sparta?
      What might they have disapproved of? _____
   _____

2. Confucius emphasized the values of social order, harmony, and respect for authority.
   What values did Athens emphasize? _____
   _____

3. To stop criticism of his government, Emperor Shi Huangdi killed scholars and
   burned "useless" books. How did the government of Athens react to Socrates'
   questioning of traditional values? _____
   _____

4. Confucius thought that education could change a poor person into a gentleman who
   could work in the civil service to help a ruler govern well.

   a. What was the goal of education in Sparta? _____

   b. What do you think should be the purpose of education? Give reasons for your answer. _____
   _____

5. Confucius thought that rulers should be virtuous and kind.

   a. What qualities did Plato think a philosopher-king should have? _____

   b. What qualities do you think a good ruler should have? Give reasons for your answer. _____
   _____

CHAPTER 5
Section 1

RETEACHING ACTIVITY *Cultures of the Mountains and the Sea*

Determining Main Ideas

The following questions deal with the development of Greek culture. Answer them in the space provided.

1. What geographic factors shaped Greek life?

    _____

    _____

2. What were some characteristics of Mycenaean civilization?

    _____

    _____

3. What role did Greek epics and mythology play in the culture?

    _____

    _____

Reading Comprehension

Find the name or term in the second column that best matches the description in the first column. Then write the letter of your answer in the blank.

4. _____ Tiryns and Athens were two cities that belonged to this civilization   a. Trojan War

5. _____ Mycenaeans' 10-year struggle with Troy, a city in Anatolia   b. epic

6. _____ Blind storyteller of Greece   c. *Iliad*

7. _____ General term for a narrative poem celebrating heroic deeds   d. Mycenaean

8. _____ Homer's great poem set against the backdrop of the Trojan War   e. Zeus

9. _____ In Greece, traditional stories about their gods   f. Homer

10. _____ The ruler of the Greek gods who lived on Mount Olympus   g. myths

Name _____ Date _____

CHAPTER
5
Section 2

RETEACHING ACTIVITY *Warring City-States*

Multiple Choice
Choose the best answer for each item. Write the letter of your answer in the blank.

_____ 1. A city-state in Greece was called a
  a. metropolis.
  b. province.
  c. satrap.
  d. polis.

_____ 2. A fortified hilltop where citizens gathered
  to discuss city government was called
  a. a metropolis.
  b. a phalanx.
  c. a stadium.
  d. an acropolis.

_____ 3. A system of government ruled by a single
  person, called a king, was known as
  a. an empire.
  b. a monarchy.
  c. a dynasty.
  d. a polis.

_____ 4. A government ruled by a small group of
  noble, land-owning families was
  a. an aristocracy.
  b. a monarchy.
  c. a polis.
  d. a democracy.

_____ 5. In Greece, a person who seized control of
  the government by appealing to the common people for support was
  a. a tyrant.
  b. a king.
  c. a dictator.
  d. a revolutionary.

_____ 6. Rule by the people became known as
  a. oligarchy.
  b. tyranny.
  c. democracy.
  d. monarchy.

_____ 7. The Athenian ruler who outlawed debt
  slavery was
  a. Draco.
  b. Solon.
  c. Darius.
  d. Cleisthenes.

_____ 8. A city-state that built a military state
  rather than a democracy was
  a. Athens.
  b. Peloponnesus.
  c. Corinth.
  d. Sparta.

_____ 9. A fighting form in which foot soldiers
  hold a spear in one hand and a shield in
  the other and stand side-by-side was a
  a. helot.
  b. tyrant.
  c. troop.
  d. phalanx.

_____10. All of the following are consequences of
  the Persian Wars *except:*
  a. Greek city-states felt a new sense of
    freedom.
  b. Delian League headquarters was moved
    to Sparta.
  c. Athens became the leader of the Delian
    League.
  d. Athens entered a golden age.

Name _____ Date _____

RETEACHING ACTIVITY *Democracy and Greece's Golden Age*

Determining Main Ideas

Choose the word that most accurately completes each sentence below. Write that word in the blank provided.

philosophers	Parthenon	tragedy
indirect democracy	philosophers	perspective
Thucydides	Plato	Pantheon
Trojan War	direct democracy	comedy
Peloponnesian War	Aristotle	Sophists
Pericles	Socrates	

1. A form of government in which citizens rule directly and not through representatives is called _____ .

2. _____ was the wise statesman who led Athens during much of its golden age.

3. A temple crafted by the sculptor Phidias to honor the goddess Athena was the _____ .

4. The Greek values of harmony, order, balance, and proportion in art served as the standard for what became known as _____ .

5. A _____ was a serious drama about common themes such as love, hate, and betrayal.

6. The greatest historian of the Greek classical age was _____ .

7. Greek city-states Athens and Sparta fought each other in the _____ .

8. Greek thinkers who were determined to seek the truth were called _____ .

9. The _____ were a group of thinkers who questioned the existence of the traditional Greek gods.

10. One thinker who developed a method of teaching using questions and answers was _____ .

11. _____ was a famous thinker who set forth his idea of a perfectly governed society in *The Republic.*

12. A philosopher who opened a school in Athens called the Lyceum was _____ .

Name _____   Date _____

CHAPTER 5

Section 4

RETEACHING ACTIVITY *Alexander's Empire*

Clarifying

Write T in the blank if the statement is true. If the statement is false, write F in the blank and then write the corrected statement on the line below it.

_____ 1. Philip II was the king of Peloponnesia who hoped to take control of Greece.

_____

_____ 2. Philip organized his troops into phalanxes armed with 18-foot pikes and prepared to attack Greece.

_____

_____ 3. The Macedonians defeated the Greeks at the battle of Chaeronea, which ended Greek independence.

_____

_____ 4. Philip's son Demosthenes proclaimed himself king of Macedonia upon Philip's death.

_____

_____ 5. Darius III attempted to lead Persian forces against the Macedonians, but failed.

_____

_____ 6. Alexander founded the city of Alexandria at the mouth of the Nile River in Egypt, one of a dozen cities he eventually named after himself.

_____

_____ 7. Alexander and his exhausted forces finally turned back toward home after winning a particularly fierce battle in Persepolis.

_____

_____ 8. Alexander died at the age of 32 during brutal fighting in Babylon.

_____

_____ 9. Three leaders took control of Alexander's empire after his death: Antigonus in Macedonia and the Greek city-states, Ptolemy in Egypt, and Seleucus in Arabia.

_____

_____ 10. Alexander's conquests brought about a vibrant new culture that blended Greek and Eastern customs.

_____

CHAPTER

5

Section 5

RETEACHING ACTIVITY *The Spread of Hellenistic Culture*

Determining Main Ideas

The following questions deal with the Hellenistic culture that flourished throughout Greece, Egypt, and Asia. Answer them in the space provided.

1. How did Alexander's conquests affect Greek culture?

    _____

2. What influences blended to form the new Hellenistic culture?

    _____

3. Which city was the center of commerce and Hellenistic civilization?

    _____

4. What attractions lured visitors to this city?

    _____

5. What significant scientific conclusions did Aristarchus, an astronomer, reach?

    _____

    _____

6. What scientific measurement did Erathosthenes, the director of the Alexandrian Library, make? How accurate was he?

    _____

7. What contributions to mathematics did Euclid make?

    _____

8. What two contributions to mathematics and physics did Archimedes make?

    _____

9. The school of philosophy called Stoicism held what beliefs?

    _____

10. What is the significance of the Colossus of Rhodes:

    _____

    _____

CHAPTER 6

Section 1

GUIDED READING *The Roman Republic*

A. *Following Chronological Order* As you read about the growth of Rome into a powerful republic, answer the questions about events in the time line. (Some dates in the time line are approximate.)

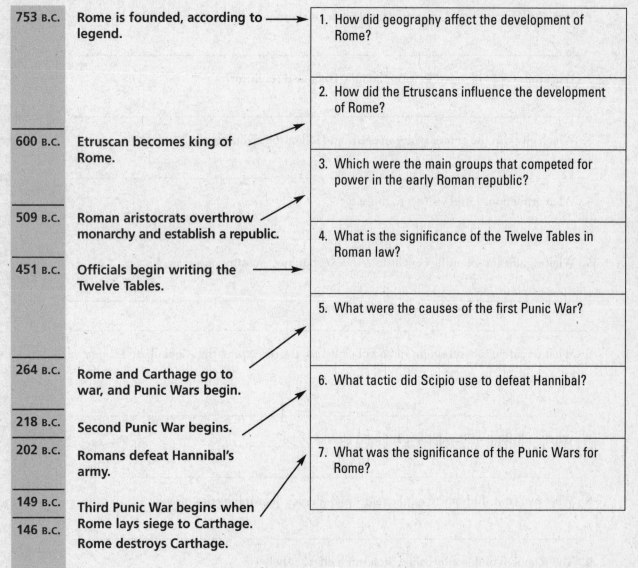

753 B.C.	Rome is founded, according to legend.
600 B.C.	Etruscan becomes king of Rome.
509 B.C.	Roman aristocrats overthrow monarchy and establish a republic.
451 B.C.	Officials begin writing the Twelve Tables.
264 B.C.	Rome and Carthage go to war, and Punic Wars begin.
218 B.C.	Second Punic War begins.
202 B.C.	Romans defeat Hannibal's army.
149 B.C.	Third Punic War begins when Rome lays siege to Carthage.
146 B.C.	Rome destroys Carthage.

1. How did geography affect the development of Rome?

2. How did the Etruscans influence the development of Rome?

3. Which were the main groups that competed for power in the early Roman republic?

4. What is the significance of the Twelve Tables in Roman law?

5. What were the causes of the first Punic War?

6. What tactic did Scipio use to defeat Hannibal?

7. What was the significance of the Punic Wars for Rome?

B. *Recognizing Main Ideas* On the back of this paper, describe the form of government the Romans established under the republic. Use the following terms.

Senate   **tribunes**   **consuls**   **dictator**

Name _____ Date _____

GUIDED READING *The Fall of the
Roman Empire*

A. *Analyzing Causes and Recognizing Effects* As you read about the decline and
   fall of the Roman Empire, take notes to answer the questions.

1. What were the causes of each condition that led to the fall of the Roman Empire?	
a. Disruption of trade	
b. Gold and silver drain	
c. Inflation	
d. Decline of loyalty and discipline in military	
e. Citizen indifference and loss of patriotism	

2. What steps did Diocletian take to restore order and reform the empire?

3. What did Constantine do to reform the empire?

4. What caused the final collapse of the Western Roman Empire?

B. *Analyzing Causes and Recognizing Effects* On the back of this paper, explain how
   mercenaries and **Attila** contributed to the decline and fall of the Roman Empire.

CHAPTER

6

Section 5

GUIDED READING *Rome and the Roots of Western Civilization*

A. *Summarizing* As you read about the roots of classical civilization, fill in the chart to identify elements of the Greco-Roman culture.

Cultural Element	Greek Contributions	Roman Contributions
1. Sculpture		
2. Philosophy		
3. Literature		

B. *Clarifying* Identify Roman achievements in the boxes below.

4. Language	5. Architecture	6. Engineering

C. *Comparing* On the back of this paper, identify **Virgil** and **Tacitus** and their contributions to Roman culture.

Name _____ Date _____

A. *Matching* Match the description in the second column with the term or name in the first column. Write the appropriate letter next to the word.

_____ 1. Virgil

_____ 2. apostle

_____ 3. Julius Caesar

_____ 4. Augustus

_____ 5. inflation

_____ 6. Hannibal

_____ 7. mercenary

_____ 8. aqueduct

a. Roman dictator whose assassination led to civil war

b. a foreign soldier who fights for money

c. Roman poet who wrote the epic, the *Aeneid*

d. one of the twelve disciples, or followers, of Jesus

e. Roman emperor whose reign initiated a long period of peace in the empire

f. Carthaginian general who crossed the Alps with elephants to fight the Romans

g. a channel for transporting water

h. a drastic drop in the value of money along with rising prices

B. *Evaluating* Write *T* in the blank if the statement is true. If the statement is false, write *F* in the blank and then write the corrected statement on the line below.

_____ 1. Greco-Roman culture, which blends elements of Greek, Hellenistic, and Roman culture, is also called classical civilization.

_____

_____ 2. The period of over 200 years during which the Roman Empire was at constant war is known as the *Pax Romana*.

_____

_____ 3. Christianity is based on the teachings of a Jew named Jesus.

_____

_____ 4. The Roman emperor Constantine ended the persecution of Christians.

_____

_____ 5. Because the Jews rebelled against Roman rule, most of them were executed in the Diaspora.

_____

C. *Writing* Write a paragraph describing the form of government that Rome had in the first century B.C. using the following terms.

republic   patrician   plebian   tribune   consul   senate

Name _____ Date _____

SKILLBUILDER PRACTICE *Summarizing*

When you summarize, you restate information in your own words, including only the main ideas and key facts, not every detail. As you read the following passage about the Germanic invasions of Rome, note the main ideas and key facts. Then write a summary of the passage in the space provided. (See Skillbuilder Handbook)

Many different groups took part in Rome's destruction: Ostrogoths, Visigoths, Franks, Angles, Saxons, Burgundians, Lombards, and Vandals. All these groups spoke Germanic languages. When Rome was still strong, the Germanic tribes generally respected the borders guarded by the Roman legions. These borders stretched across Europe from the Black Sea to the North Sea. For many years, the Danube River divided the Germanic tribes in the north from their Roman neighbors to the south.

Though fearless fighters, the Germanic tribes feared the Huns, a nomadic people from central Asia. When the Huns began to move west, they first attacked the Ostrogoths, the most easterly Germanic tribe. The terrified Ostrogoths fled westward and pressed against their old enemies,

the Visigoths, Pushed off their land, the Visigoths looked for a new home south of the Danube River. Thus began the massive movement of Germanic people that eventually destroyed the western half of the Roman Empire. In A.D. 378, the Visigoths scored a victory against the Roman army and shattered Rome's military reputation.

The Huns kept raiding westward, destroying as they went. Germanic peoples near the Rhine—Burgundians, Frank, and Vandals—were forced to move. Bundled in furs, some 15,000 Vandal warriors and their families crossed the frozen Rhine River in the winter of 406. Meeting little resistance, they traveled west into the Roman province of Gaul. They raided the cities of Gaul as if they were defenseless and easily subdued Gaul's population of about 20 million.

Write your summary of the passage here.

_____

_____

_____

_____

_____

_____

_____

_____

_____

_____

_____

_____

_____

Name _____ Date _____

GEOGRAPHY APPLICATION: MOVEMENT

The Roads of the Roman Empire

Section 2   *Directions: Read the paragraphs below and study the map. Then answer the questions that follow.*

The famous Roman roads were a vast network of hard-surfaced roads connecting the city of Rome to the farthest reaches of its empire. The stone-paved highways lasted for more than a thousand years, and some sections are still in use today. Author Isaac Asimov claimed that there was no better mode of transportation in the world until the arrival of railroads close to 2,000 years later. Romans began building roads in 312 B.C. following their first major conquests. The beginning stretch, the Appian Way, trailed 132 miles southeast out of Rome. Thereafter, roadbuilding kept pace with the

empire's expansion. Eventually, Roman roads wound 53,000 miles around the Mediterranean and northeastern Atlantic regions.

The roads, constructed by slaves and soldiers, were wide enough for large wagons to pass each other. The principal use of the highways was to move Roman armies from one part of the empire to another. However, citizens were free to use the roads. The Roman statesman Cicero once spoke of moving 56 miles in a cart in just ten hours. However, travelers had to be alert for bandits, as people might simply "disappear" while riding on Roman roads.

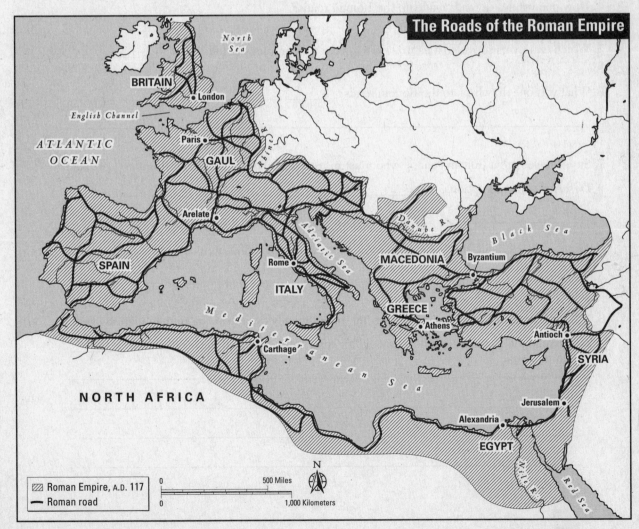

The Roads of the Roman Empire

Ancient Rome and Early Christianity 33

Interpreting Text and Visuals

1. How is the area of the Roman Empire shown? _____

   What symbol represents roads on the map? _____

2. What is the approximate straight-line distance in miles between Paris and Rome? _____

   What is the approximate distance between the two cities along the Roman roads, choosing the

   route that passes by Arelate? _____

3. Describe the location of the four significant breaks for bodies of water that the map shows in the

   Roman road system. _____

   _____

   _____

4. How many miles of roads made up the Roman roads? _____

5. Which two rivers provided a natural path for the Roman roads to follow? _____

6. What was one drawback to the Roman roads? _____

   _____

7. Suppose you are a Roman general who must move a legion of soldiers from Rome to Carthage.

   Describe your two options. _____

   _____

   _____

   _____

8. "All roads lead to Rome" is a famous saying that originally described the Roman highway system.

   Why would the Romans have developed their road network with Rome as its focus? _____

   _____

   _____

   _____

   _____

CHAPTER

6

Section 2

PRIMARY SOURCE *from The Gallic War*
by Julius Caesar

Julius Caesar's account of his military campaigns is a valuable historical record left by a great Roman general. As you read Caesar's account of the second Roman invasion of Britain during his campaign to conquer what is now France, notice that he refers to himself in the third person.

14. Of all the Britons the most civilized are those in Kent, all of which is along the coast. Their habits do not differ much from the Gauls'. The inland people do not sow grain but live on milk and meat and wear skins. All Britons stain themselves with woad, which makes them blue and more terrifying to confront in battle. Their hair they wear long, but they shave all the rest of their bodies except the head and upper lip. . . .

15. The enemy horse and chariots engaged our cavalry briskly on the march, but our men everywhere had the upper hand and drove them into the forests and hills. But when they had killed a number they pursued too eagerly and lost some of their own. But after an interval they suddenly dashed from the forest to fall upon our unsuspecting men, who were busy entrenching their camp, and delivered a sharp attack upon the pickets posted in front of the camp. Caesar supported them with two cohorts, each the chief of its legion. These took position with only a small space between them, but while our men were confounded by their novel mode of fighting, they boldly broke through their midst and then retired without loss. . . .

16. This engagement, fought in front of the camp in full view of everyone, made it plain that our men were not a fit match for such adversaries. They could not pursue an advantage because of their heavy armor; . . . nor could our cavalry engage except at great peril, for the Britons would purposely retreat, and when they had drawn our cavalry a little distance from the legionaries, leap down from their chariots and exploit the advantage of fighting on foot. In a cavalry engagement this tactic involved equal danger whether we pursued or retreated. Another disadvantage was that they never fought in a mass but widely scattered. . . .

17. On the next day the enemy took position at a distance in the hills; they showed themselves only in small groups, and attacked our cavalry with less energy than the day before. At noon, when Caesar had sent three legions and all the cavalry under command of Gaius Trebonius to forage, they suddenly swooped down on the foragers from all directions, even up to the legions and standards. Our men counterattacked vigorously, beat them back, and pressed their pursuit, seeing the legions close behind to support them. They drove the enemy headlong and killed a large number, giving them no chance to rally and make a stand . . .

18. Apprised now of their plan, Caesar marched his army to the territory of Cassivellaunus towards the Thames, a river which can be forded on foot at only one point, and that with difficulty. Upon his arrival there he observed a large enemy force drawn up on the far bank. The bank was protected by sharp stakes fixed in the ground, and there were similar stakes in the river bed, covered by the water. This Caesar had learned from prisoners and deserters. He sent his cavalry forward and ordered the legions to follow at their heels. Though only their heads were above water, they moved with such speed and dash that the enemy could not sustain the assault of legions and cavalry, abandoned the bank, and took to flight.

from Julius Caesar, *The Gallic War and Other Writings*, Moses Hadas trans. (New York: The Modern Library, 1957), 102–104.

Discussion Questions
Determining Main Ideas
1. According to Caesar, what military advantages and disadvantages did the Britons have?
2. What military advantages and disadvantages did the Romans have?
3. *Forming and Supporting Opinions* Do you think this excerpt supports the notion that Caesar was a genius at military strategy? Explain your answer.

Ancient Rome and Early Christianity 35

CHAPTER 6

Section 3

PRIMARY SOURCE Emperor Galerius's Edict of Toleration

During the third century and the early years of the fourth century, Roman rulers cruelly persecuted Christians. Despite repression, the religion continued to thrive and spread. In A.D. 311, Emperor Galerius issued the first edict, or formal proclamation, of toleration of Christianity just a few days before his death. Why did Galerius decide to tolerate Christians?

Amongst our other measures for the advantage of the Empire, we have hitherto endeavored to bring all things into conformity with the ancient laws and public order of the Romans. We have been especially anxious that even the Christians, who have abandoned the religion of their ancestors, should return to reason. For they have fallen, we know not how, into such perversity and folly that, instead of adhering to those ancient institutions which possibly their own forefathers established, they have arbitrarily made laws of their own and collected together various peoples from various quarters.

After the publication, on our part, of an order commanding Christians to return to the observance of the ancient customs, many of them, it is true, submitted in view of the danger, while many others suffered death. Nevertheless, since many of them have continued to persist in their opinions and we see that in the present situation they neither duly adore and venerate the gods nor yet worship the god of the Christians, we, with our wonted clemency, have judged it is wise to extend a pardon even to these men and permit them once more to become Christians and reëstablish their places of meetings; in such manner, however, that they shall in no way offend against good order. We propose to notify the magistrates in another mandate in regard to the course that they should pursue.

Whereof it should be the duty of the Christians, in view of our clemency, to pray to their god for our welfare, for that of the Empire, and for their own, so that the Empire may remain intact in all its parts, and that they themselves may live safely in their habitations.

from Milton Viorst, ed., *The Great Documents of Western Civilization* (New York: Bantam, 1965), 6.

Activity Options

1. ***Determining Main Ideas*** With several classmates, role-play Christians who live in the Roman empire in A.D. 311. Discuss your reactions to Galerius's edict.

2. ***Analyzing Issues*** Make a two-column chart. List what Galerius offered Christians in one column and what he asked in return in the other column. Then discuss with classmates whether or not this edict was fair.

CHAPTER
6
Section 4

PRIMARY SOURCE Dinner with Attila the Hun
from Historici Graeci Minores
by Priscus

In about A.D. 450, representatives from the western and eastern parts of the Roman Empire met with Attila, the king of the Huns, on a special diplomatic mission. Priscus, a representative of the eastern Roman Empire, wrote an account of having dinner with Attila. What do you learn about Attila from this account?

Attila invited both parties of us to dine with him about three o'clock that afternoon. We waited for the time of the invitation, and then all of us, the envoys from the Western Romans as well, presented ourselves in the doorway facing Attila. In accordance with the national custom the cupbearers gave us a cup for us to make our libations before we took our seats. When that had been done and we had sipped the wine, we went to the chairs where we would sit to have dinner. All the seats were ranged down either side of the room, up against the walls. In the middle Attila was sitting on a couch with a second couch behind him. Behind that a few steps led up to his bed, which for decorative purposes was covered in ornate drapes made of fine linen, like those which Greeks and Romans prepare for marriage ceremonies. I think that the more distinguished guests were on Attila's right, and the second rank on his left, where we were with Berichos, a man of some renown among the Scythians, who was sitting in front of us. Onegesios was to the right of Attila's couch, and opposite him were two of the king's sons on chairs. The eldest son was sitting on Attila's own couch, right on the very edge, with his eyes fixed on the ground in fear of his father. . . .
After everyone had been toasted, the cupbearers left, and a table was put in front of Attila and other tables for groups of three or four men each. This enabled each guest to help himself to the things put on the table without leaving his proper seat. Attila's servant entered first with plates full of meat, and those waiting on all the others put bread and cooked food on the tables. A lavish meal, served on silver trenchers, was prepared for us and the other barbarians, but Attila just had some meat on a wooden platter, for this was one aspect of his self-discipline. For instance, gold or silver cups were presented to the other diners, but his own goblet was made of wood. His clothes, too, were simple,

and no trouble was taken except to have them clean. The sword that hung by his side, the clasps of his barbarian shoes and the bridle of his horse were all free from gold, precious stones or other valuable decorations affected by the other Scythians. When the food in the first plates was finished we all got up, and no one, once on his feet, returned to his seat until he had, in the same order as before, drunk the full cup of wine that he was handed, with a toast for Attila's health. After this honour had been paid him, we sat down again and second plates were put on each table with other food on them. This also finished, everyone rose once more, drank another toast and resumed his seat.
As twilight came on torches were lit, and two barbarians entered before Attila to sing some songs they had composed, telling of his victories and his valour in war. The guests paid close attention to them, and some were delighted with the songs, others excited at being reminded of the wars, but others broke down and wept if their bodies were weakened by age and their warrior spirits forced to remain inactive.

from B. K. Workman, trans., *They Saw It Happen in Classical Times* (Basil Blackwell Ltd., 1964). Reprinted in John Carey, ed., *Eyewitness to History* (New York: Avon Books, 1987), 23–24.

Activity Options

1. *Summarizing* With your classmates, plan and then present a re-creation of Priscus's dinner with Attila. Portray Attila, his servants, his sons, other Huns, the singers, and representatives of the western and eastern parts of the Roman Empire. Draw on details in the passage to bring this re-enactment to life.
2. *Comparing and Contrasting* Make a Venn diagram comparing and contrasting Attila with the other diners.

CHAPTER 6

Section 5

PRIMARY SOURCE The Eruption of Vesuvius
Letter from Pliny the Younger to Tacitus

In A.D. 79 Mount Vesuvius, a volcano in southwest Italy, erupted, burying the cities of Pompeii and Herculaneum. Among those killed was Roman historian C. Plinius Secundus, known as Pliny the Elder. His nephew, Pliny the Younger, wrote an account of the disaster in a letter to the Roman historian Tacitus. As you read part of his letter, think about the dangers Pliny's uncle faced.

Your request that I would send you an account of my uncle's death, in order to transmit a more exact relation of it to posterity, deserves my acknowledgments; for, if this accident shall be celebrated by your pen, the glory of it, I am well assured, will be rendered forever illustrious. . . . On the 24th of August, about one in the afternoon, my mother desired him to observe a cloud which appeared of a very unusual size and shape. . . . This phenomenon seemed to a man of such learning and research as my uncle extraordinary and worth further looking into. . . . He ordered the galleys to be put to sea, and went himself on board. . . . Hastening then to the place from whence others fled with the utmost terror, he steered his course direct to the point of danger, and with so much calmness and presence of mind as to be able to make and dictate his observations upon the motion and all the phenomena of that dreadful scene. . . . [The wind] was favourable, however, for carrying my uncle to Pomponianus, whom he found in the greatest consternation. . . . Meanwhile broad flames shone out in several places from Mount Vesuvius, which the darkness of the night contributed to render still brighter and clearer. But my uncle, in order to soothe the apprehensions of his friend, assured him it was only the burning of the villages, which the country people had abandoned to the flames; after this he retired to rest. . . . The court which led to his apartment being now almost filled with stones and ashes, if he had continued there any time longer, it would have been impossible for him to have made his way out. So he was awoke and got up, and went to Pomponianus and the rest of his company. . . . They consulted together whether it would be most prudent to trust to the houses, which now rocked from side to side with frequent and violent concussions as though shaken from their very foundations; or fly to the open fields, where the calcined stones and cinders, though light indeed, yet fell in large showers, and threatened destruction. In this choice of dangers they resolved for the fields: a resolution which, while the rest of the company were hurried into by their fears, my uncle embraced upon cool and deliberate consideration. They went out then, having pillows tied upon their heads with napkins; and this was their whole defense against the storm of stones that fell round them. It was now day everywhere else, but there a deeper darkness prevailed than in the thickest night. . . . They thought proper to go farther down upon the shore. . . . There my uncle, laying himself down upon a sail cloth, which was spread for him, called twice for some cold water, which he drank, when immediately the flames, preceded by a strong whiff of sulphur, dispersed the rest of the party, and obliged him to rise. He raised himself up with the assistance of two of his servants, and instantly fell down dead; suffocated, as I conjecture, by some gross and noxious vapour. . . . As soon as it was light again, which was not till the third day after this melancholy accident, his body was found entire, and without any marks of violence upon it, in the dress in which he fell, and looking more like a man asleep than dead. . . . I will end here, only adding that I have faithfully related to you what I was either an eye-witness of myself or received immediately after the accident happened, and before there was time to vary the truth. You will pick out of this narrative whatever is most important: for a letter is one thing, a history another; it is one thing writing to a friend, another thing writing to the public. Farewell.

from William Melmoth, trans., *Letters of Gaius Plinius Caecilius Secundus* (New York: Collier, 1909), 298–302.

Research Options

1. ***Using Research in Writing*** Find out about Pliny the Elder, Pliny the Younger, or Tacitus. Write a brief biographical sketch of this person.
2. ***Analyzing Cause and Effect*** Read more about Mount Vesuvius. Then create a cause-and-effect diagram to illustrate your findings.

Name _____ Date _____

CHAPTER 6 — Section 2

LITERATURE SELECTION *from* **Julius Caesar**
by William Shakespeare

English poet and playwright William Shakespeare (1564–1616) drew heavily on a translation of classical biographer Plutarch's The Lives of the Noble Grecians and Romans *for information about the Roman characters in Julius Caesar. Shakespeare's tragedy, which was first performed in 1599, traces events before and after Caesar's death. In Act 3, Scene 2, from which this excerpt is taken, Brutus first speaks at Caesar's funeral to explain why he helped assassinate Caesar. Mark Antony, one of Caesar's supporters, then delivers a powerful address. As you read his speech, think about how Mark Antony reacts to Caesar's murder and how he stirs the crowd of Romans.*

ANTONY: Friends, Romans, countrymen, lend me
   your ears.
I come to bury Caesar, not to praise him.
The evil that men do lives after them;
The good is oft interrèd with their bones.
So let it be with Caesar. The noble Brutus
Hath told you Caesar was ambitious.
If it were so, it was a grievous fault,
And grievously hath Caesar answered it.
Here, under leave of Brutus and the rest—
For Brutus is an honorable man,
So are they all, all honorable men—
Come I to speak in Caesar's funeral.
He was my friend, faithful and just to me;
But Brutus says he was ambi-
   tious,
And Brutus is an honorable
   man.
He hath brought many captives
   home to Rome,
Whose ransoms did the general
   coffers fill.
Did this in Caesar seem ambitious?
When that the poor have cried, Caesar hath wept;
Ambition should be made of sterner stuff.
Yet Brutus says he was ambitious,
And Brutus is an honorable man.
You all did see that on the Lupercal
I thrice presented him a kingly crown,
Which he did thrice refuse. Was this ambition?
Yet Brutus says he was ambitious,
And sure he is an honorable man.
I speak not to disprove what Brutus spoke,
But here I am to speak what I do know.
You all did love him once, not without cause.
What cause withholds you then to mourn for
   him?

> *"I come to bury Caesar, not to praise him."*

O judgment! Thou art fled to brutish beasts,
And men have lost their reason. Bear with me;
My heart is in the coffin there with Caesar,
And I must pause till it come back to me.
FIRST PLEBEIAN: Methinks there is much reason
   in his sayings.
SECOND PLEBEIAN: If thou consider rightly of the
   matter,
Caesar has had great wrong.
THIRD PLEBEIAN: Has he, masters?
I fear there will a worse come in his place.
FOURTH PLEBEIAN: Marked ye his words? He
   would not take the crown,
Therefore 'tis certain he was not ambitious.
FIRST PLEBEIAN: If it be found so,
   some will dear abide it.
SECOND PLEBEIAN: Poor soul, his
   eyes are red as fire with weep-
   ing.
THIRD PLEBEIAN: There's not a
   nobler man in Rome than Antony.
FOURTH PLEBEIAN: Now mark him. He begins
   again to speak.
ANTONY: But yesterday the word of Caesar might
   Have stood against the world. Now lies he there,
   And none so poor to do him reverence.
   O masters! If I were disposed to stir
   Your hearts and minds to mutiny and rage,
   I should do Brutus wrong, and Cassius wrong,
   Who, you all know, are honorable men.
   I will not do them wrong; I rather choose
   To wrong the dead, to wrong myself and you,
   Than I will wrong such honorable men.
   But here's a parchment with the seal of Caesar.
   I found it in his closet; 'tis his will.
[He shows the will.]
   Let but the commons hear this testament—

Ancient Rome and Early Christianity **39**

Which, pardon me, I do not mean to read—
And they would go and kiss dead Caesar's
wounds
And dip their napkins in his sacred blood,
Yea, beg a hair of him for memory,
And dying, mention it within their wills,
Bequeathing it as a rich legacy
Unto their issue.

FOURTH PLEBEIAN: We'll hear the will! Read it,
Mark Antony.

ALL: The will, the will! We will hear Caesar's will.

ANTONY: Have patience, gentle friends; I must not
read it.
It is not meet you know how Caesar loved you.
You are not wood, you are not stones, but men;
And being men, hearing the will of Caesar,
It will inflame you, it will make you mad.
'Tis good you know not that you are his heirs,
For if you should, O, what
would come of it?

FOURTH PLEBEIAN: Read the will!
We'll hear it, Antony.
You shall read us the will,
Caesar's will.

ANTONY: Will you be patient?
Will you stay awhile?
I have o'ershot myself to tell you of it.
I fear I wrong the honorable men
Whose daggers have stabbed Caesar; I do fear it.

FOURTH PLEBEIAN: They were traitors.
"Honorable men"!

ALL: The will! The testament!

SECOND PLEBEIAN: They were villains, murderers.
The will! Read the will!

ANTONY: You will compel me then to read the will?
Then make a ring about the corpse of Caesar
And let me show you him that made the will.
Shall I descend? And will you give me leave?

ALL: Come down.

SECOND PLEBEIAN: Descend.

THIRD PLEBEIAN: You shall have leave.

[Antony comes down. They gather around Caesar.]

FOURTH PLEBEIAN: A ring; stand round.

FIRST PLEBEIAN: Stand from the hearse. Stand
from the body.

SECOND PLEBEIAN: Room for Antony, most noble
Antony!

ANTONY: Nay, press not so upon me. Stand far off.

ALL: Stand back! Room! Bear back!

ANTONY: If you have tears, prepare to shed them
now.

*"If you have tears,
prepare to shed
them now."*

You all do know this mantle. I remember
The first time ever Caesar put it on;
'Twas on a summer's evening in his tent,
That day he overcame the Nervii.
Look, in this place ran Cassius' dagger through.
See what a rent the envious Casca made.
Through this the well-belovèd Brutus stabbed,
And as he plucked his cursèd steel away,
Mark how the blood of Caesar followed it,
As rushing out of doors to be resolved
If Brutus so unkindly knocked or no;
For Brutus, as you know, was Caesar's angel.
Judge, O you gods, how dearly Caesar loved him!
This was the most unkindest cut of all;
For when the noble Caesar saw him stab,
Ingratitude, more strong than traitors' arms,
Quite vanquished him. Then burst his mighty
heart,
And in his mantle muffling up his
face,
Even at the base of Pompey's stat-
ue,
Which all the while ran blood,
great Caesar fell.
O, what a fall was there, my coun-
trymen!
Then I, and you, and all of us fell down,
Whilst bloody treason flourished over us.
O, now you weep, and I perceive you feel
The dint of pity. These are gracious drops.
Kind souls, what weep you when you but behold
Our Caesar's vesture wounded? Look you here,
Here is himself, marred as you see with traitors.

[He lifts Caesar's mantle.]

FIRST PLEBEIAN: O piteous spectacle!

SECOND PLEBEIAN: O noble Caesar!

THIRD PLEBEIAN: O woeful day!

FOURTH PLEBEIAN: O traitors, villains!

FIRST PLEBEIAN: O most bloody sight!

SECOND PLEBEIAN: We will be revenged.

ALL: Revenge! About! Seek! Burn! Fire! Kill! Slay!
Let not a traitor live!

ANTONY: Stay, countrymen.

FIRST PLEBEIAN: Peace there! Hear the noble
Antony.

SECOND PLEBEIAN: We'll hear him, we'll follow
him,
we'll die with him!

ANTONY: Good friends, sweet friends, let me not
stir you up
To such a sudden flood of mutiny

They that have done this deed are honorable.
What private griefs they have, alas, I know not,
That made them do it. They are wise and
  honorable,
And will no doubt with reasons answer you.
I come not, friends, to steal away your hearts.
I am no orator, as Brutus is,
But, as you know me all, a plain blunt man
That love my friend, and that they know full well
That gave me public leave to speak of him.
For I have neither wit, nor words, nor worth,
Action, nor utterance, nor the power of speech
To stir men's blood. I only speak right on.
I tell you that which you yourselves do know,
Show you sweet Caesar's wounds, poor poor
  dumb mouths,
And bid them speak for me. But were I Brutus,
And Brutus Antony, there were an Antony
Would ruffle up your spirits and put a tongue
In every wound of Caesar that should move
The stones of Rome to rise and mutiny.
ALL: We'll mutiny!
FIRST PLEBEIAN: We'll burn the house of Brutus!
THIRD PLEBEIAN: Away, then! Come, seek the
  conspirators.
Antony: Yet hear me, countrymen. Yet hear me
  speak.

ALL: Peace, ho! Hear Antony, most noble Antony!
ANTONY: Why, friends, you go to do you know not
  what.
  Wherein hath Caesar thus deserved your loves?
  Alas, you know not. I must tell you then:
  You have forgot the will I told you of.
ALL: Most true, the will! Let's stay and hear the will.
ANTONY: Here is the will, and under Caesar's seal.
  To every Roman citizen he gives,
  To every several man, seventy-five drachmas.
SECOND PLEBEIAN: Most noble Caesar! We'll
  revenge his death.

Activity Options

1. *Describing Plot, Setting, and Character*
   With a group of classmates, plan, rehearse, and
   give a performance of this excerpt for your class.
2. *Drawing Conclusions* Make a sketch of a costume that a character in this excerpt might wear.
   Display your finished costume design.

CHAPTER 6

Section 2

HISTORYMAKERS Cleopatra
Wily Queen of Egypt

"To know her was to be touched with an irresistible charm. Her form, . . . the persuasiveness of her conversation, and her delightful . . . behavior—all these produced a blend of magic."—Plutarch, a Roman historian

Cleopatra, queen of Egypt, has gone down in history as a conniving leader who used tricks to gain influence within the Roman Empire. She was actually an intelligent ruler who used an iron will in an effort to keep Egypt free of Roman control. Ironically, the queen who tried to preserve Egypt was not even Egyptian. Cleopatra belonged to the family of the Ptolemies. This family from Macedon had ruled Egypt for several hundred years after the death of Alexander the Great. Though they had ruled Egypt for a long time, none of the family had ever bothered to learn Egyptian—until Cleopatra. Plutarch wrote that she learned so many languages she could speak to "Ethiopians, Troglodytes, Jews, Arabs, Syrians, Medes, and Parthians" in their own tongues.

In the first century B.C., the family's fortunes and its hold on Egypt declined. Cleopatra's father was a weak king. He showed more interest in music than in running his kingdom, leading the people to nickname him "the Flute Player." He feared that Rome would seize Egypt, an attractive place because of its abundance of farmland. To buy safety, he sent huge amounts of money as bribes to various Roman leaders, including Julius Caesar. He eventually died in 51 B.C. At the time, Cleopatra was 18.

She became queen, ruling along with her brother Ptolemy XIII, who was only ten. Powerful insiders in the Egyptian court hoped to run the country by controlling the young king. They forced Cleopatra to flee Egypt three years later.

However, she raised an army and prepared to retake her crown, ready to fight her brother for control. Meanwhile, Julius Caesar had defeated his rivals and become the powerful leader of Rome. When Caesar came to Egypt to settle the issue of the throne, Cleopatra seized her chance to argue her case. She had herself wrapped in a rug and carried to Caesar so she could speak to him directly. Impressed by her clever and bold act, Caesar agreed to back her rather than her brother. Caesar and Cleopatra also began a relationship. They may have loved one another, but one historian cautioned,

"it must always be borne in mind that both of them were ruthless and devious politicians." Later, she had a son that was Caesar's. He was named Caesarion. Cleopatra's brother died fighting Caesar's army, and in 47 B.C. she was back on the throne. She and Caesar may have planned to marry and become king and queen of Rome with Caesarion to follow them. In 44 B.C., however, those hopes were destroyed. Caesar was assassinated by senators who wished to restore the Roman Republic. Cleopatra, in Rome at the time, decided it was wise to return to Egypt. Caesar's heir, Octavian, and his friend Mark Antony began to rule Rome together. The two leaders had an uneasy alliance, however, and each tried to outfox the other in order to gain control of the Roman government. Cleopatra enchanted Antony as she had Caesar. By 37 B.C., Antony had dismissed his wife, married Cleopatra, and recognized her two children as his own. He also gave large amounts of land to her, restoring Cyprus and Lebanon to Egypt. The wife that Antony rejected, however, was the sister of Octavian. This drove a wedge between the former allies. With Cleopatra's wealth Antony rebuilt his army and navy. In 31 B.C., his forces met Octavian's in battle to decide who would control Rome—and thus the Mediterranean. Octavian won, and Cleopatra and Antony escaped back to Egypt. Octavian, though, brought his armies there the following year. Trapped and unable to win, Antony committed suicide. Cleopatra pleaded with Octavian to allow her to retire and make Caesarion king of Egypt. Octavian refused, and she too committed suicide. Soon after, Octavian had Caesarion killed.

Questions

1. **Contrasting** How was Cleopatra different from the other members of the Ptolemaic Dynasty?
2. **Making Inferences** Why was Rome so important to the fate of Cleopatra's Egypt?
3. **Drawing Conclusions** Why did Octavian have Caesarion killed?

CHAPTER 6

Section 2

HISTORYMAKERS Julius Caesar
General, Writer, Politician, Dictator-King?

"Caesar could no longer endure a superior, nor Pompey an equal."—Lucan, a
Roman poet, on the cause of the Roman civil war

Driven by ambition and a thirst for power, Julius Caesar became a great and controversial leader of the Roman Republic. He had a tremendous impact on a growing power at a crucial point in its rise. He was also a man of extraordinary abilities—skills in war, politics, writing, and leadership. Caesar was born to an old Roman family, part of the group of families that founded the Roman Republic. He had the standard education of someone in his social position and became known as a charming, cultured, and well-read person. In addition, he gained experience in the military in Asia Minor and experience in government in Spain. Gradually, he won election to important public offices. In 63 B.C., he was voted pontifex maximus, the chief priest of the Republic. He also served in Spain, where he won fame by winning battles. He returned to Rome and was elected consul, the most important political office in the Republic.

Caesar joined with two other leading Romans in an alliance. One was Crassus, a wealthy political leader whose money could be used to advance the plans of the three. The other was Pompey, another brilliant general. To cement the alliance, Pompey married Julia, Caesar's only daughter.

As consul, Caesar worked for some new laws that eased the overcrowding in Rome and other cities. He was rewarded by being made governor of Gaul, located in modern France. He took command of the Roman armies there, determined to extend Roman control of the area. It took several years, but he eventually conquered all of Gaul and part of Britain.

The victories brought Caesar riches, which he used to fund building projects in Rome—thus winning popularity in the city. He also made sure to create some effective propaganda in his own favor. He wrote *Commentaries on the Gallic Wars*, a history of his campaigns in Gaul. Throughout the book, he referred to himself as "Caesar" and not as "I." This made the history seem objective. He also made sure that "Caesar" got credit for all victories.

The situation in Rome, however, had changed. Julia had died, which removed one link between Pompey and Caesar. Crassus had died as well. The two generals now became bitter rivals for power. The senate, controlled by Pompey, gave Caesar a difficult choice. It ordered him to give his armies to another general, and return to Rome if he wanted to stand for election to consul again. He decided to ignore the senate and lead his army into Italy. Years of civil war followed. Pompey was backed by many major political leaders. Caesar, however, had another resource: an experienced, tough army. Pompey fled Italy for the east, where Caesar won a major victory. Pompey then retreated further to Egypt. There he was treacherously killed by a one-time supporter, Ptolemy XIII (the pharaoh of Egypt and brother to Cleopatra). In 46 B.C., Caesar defeated another army in Africa, and the following year he won victory over the sons of Pompey in Spain. Caesar was named dictator for life. As supreme ruler of Rome, he passed many reforms. However, many senators opposed him. Some simply disliked him and resented his power. Others feared that he planned to make himself king. In February, 44 B.C., he presided over a festival. By plan, Mark Antony, a close ally, offered him a king's crown. The watching crowd stirred restlessly. When Caesar refused it, they cheered. Antony again offered it, Caesar again refused it, and the crowd cheered. Still, Caesar moved behind the scenes to try to have himself made king. He also prepared to lead an army east for more conquests. On his last day in Rome, one month after the festival, his planning came to an end. As he entered the senate, a group of senators fell on him. They stabbed him 23 times. He died, ironically, at the foot of a statue of Pompey.

Questions

1. *Clarifying* How did Caesar show he was a brilliant general?
2. *Drawing Conclusions* How did Caesar use his success in Gaul to improve his political position in Rome?
3. *Determining Main Ideas* Why did the senators oppose Caesar?

Ancient Rome and Early Christianity 43

Name _____ Date _____

CONNECTIONS ACROSS TIME AND CULTURES

CHAPTER **6** Section 5

Hellenistic Culture and Roman Culture

THEMATIC CONNECTION:
POWER AND AUTHORITY

As you learned in Chapter 5, the Hellenistic culture emerged as elements of Greek culture blended with Egyptian, Persian, and Indian influences. As you learned in this chapter, the Romans preserved and expanded many Hellenistic values within their own culture and developed unique accomplishments of their own.

A. Listed below are some of the major legacies of Hellenistic culture and of Roman culture. Use the Venn diagram to sort those cultural accomplishments. Two are already in their proper places. (One is shared by both cultures.) Then answer the question that follows.

Cultural Accomplishments	
1. Organized central government of a unified empire	6. Created system of law
2. Made discoveries in mathematics and physics	7. Created fine mosaic art work
3. Influenced by Greek culture	8. Built extensive system of roads
4. Created philosophies of Stoicism and Epicureanism	9. Created famous museum and library
5. Made realistic portrait sculptures	10. Computed circumference of earth

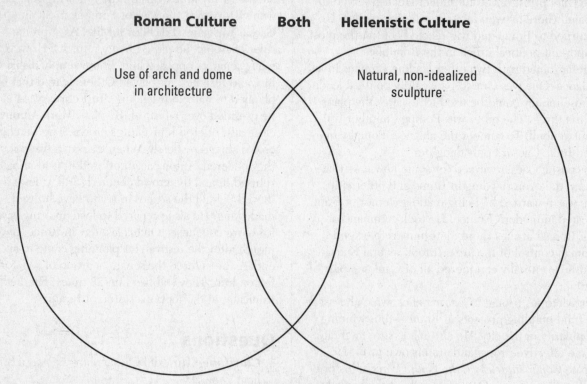

B. In your opinion, what is the main difference between Hellenistic culture and Roman culture?

_____

_____

CHAPTER
6

Section 5

SCIENCE & TECHNOLOGY *Roman Construction Technology*

The Colosseum was not the only example of Roman architectural genius. The Romans fashioned other buildings that were both monumental in size and contained new advances in structural engineering.

Around A.D. 126, Emperor Hadrian sought to honor the Roman gods by building a great temple in their honor. He constructed the Pantheon, which comes from the Greek word *pantheion*, meaning place for all gods. It was actually built from a much smaller temple that had been erected in 27 B.C. by Marcus Agrippa, the nephew of Emperor Augustus. The Pantheon is a marvel of Roman engineering, and many of the techniques pioneered in its construction are still used today.

The front of the building includes three rows of massive Corinthian columns. Each column weighs 60 tons and is 41 feet high and five feet across. On top of these supports sits a huge triangular roof.

The masterpiece of the building is one of the largest domes made of stone and concrete ever built. It covers a circular chamber, or rotunda, that is proportioned like a perfect sphere. The chamber is 142 feet across, and the top of the ceiling is 142 feet high. The dome is massive. It weighs over 5,000 tons and has walls 20 feet wide at the base that taper to five feet at the top.

The dome was constructed by pouring increasingly smaller rings of concrete, one on top of another, into a series of wooden molds. In the Middle Ages, a popular story was told about how Hadrian schemed to have this temple completed as fast as possible. The story said that the Pantheon was built around a big mound of dirt, which gave the temple support during construction. Hadrian supposedly mixed gold coins in with that soil in order to speed the workers through the final stage of building. In an attempt to find the money, the workers would quickly remove the earth from inside the temple.

Hadrian left a 29-foot wide round opening at the top. This opening, called an oculus, let sunlight

stream into the chamber and illuminate the 140 shiny bronze panels set into the ceiling. One historian stated, "[The] opening. . . doubtlessly symbolized the all-seeing eye of heaven. The building is an exemplary statement of Hadrian's world, ideated and symbolized—earth, sky, cosmos, empire—with all the Greco-Roman gods looking benevolently on Rome."

Questions

Determining Main Ideas

1. What was Hadrian's purpose for building the Pantheon?
2. What is the great architectural achievement of the Pantheon?
3. *Making Inferences* What aspect of the Pantheon might give you the feeling that it was a temple to honor the Roman gods?

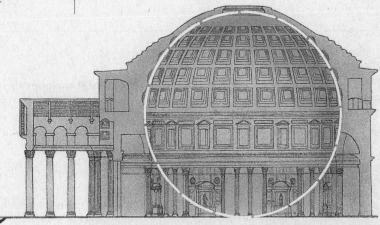

Illustration by Patrick Whelan.

Shown above is the Pantheon. The opening in the roof is the oculus, which floods the room with light. The chamber was proportioned like a perfect circle.

Ancient Rome and Early Christianity **45**

Name _____ Date _____

CHAPTER 6 Section 1

RETEACHING ACTIVITY *The Roman Republic*

Determining Main Ideas

The following questions deal with the early Roman republic. Answer them in the space provided.

1. What characterizes a republic as a form of government?

_____

_____

2. What were the differences between the patricians and the plebians in the Roman republic?

_____

_____

3. Who fought in the Punic Wars, what was the end result, and why was that end result significant?

_____

_____

4. What actions showed that Hannibal was a brilliant military strategist?

_____

_____

Reading Comprehension

Find the name or term in the second column that best matches the description in the first column. Then write the letter of your answer in the blank.

_____ 5. commanded the army and directed the government of the Roman republic

_____ 6. aristocratic branch of Rome's government

_____ 7. in the Roman republic, a leader in times of crisis who had absolute power to make laws and command the army

_____ 8. government in which citizens have the right to vote

_____ 9. large military unit of armed foot soldiers

_____ 10. elected representatives of plebians

a. republic

b. consuls

c. legions

d. tribunes

e. senate

f. dictator

Name _____ Date _____

A. *Following Chronological Order* As you read about the Mauryan and Gupta empires in India, take notes to answer the questions about the time line. (Some dates on the time line are approximate.)

321 B.C. Chandragupta Maurya claims the throne and the Mauryan Dynasty begins.	1. How did Chandragupta support his successful war efforts?
301 B.C. Chandragupta's son assumes the throne.	2. How did Chandragupta hold his vast empire together?
	3. Why did Asoka wage war early in his reign?
269 B.C. Asoka, Chandragupta's grandson, becomes king of the Mauryan Empire.	
232 B.C. Asoka dies and the empire begins to break up.	4. How did Asoka show concern for his subjects' well-being?
	5. What did Chandra Gupta I accomplish during his reign?
A.D. 320 Chandra Gupta I becomes first Gupta emperor.	
A.D. 335 Chandra Gupta's son Samudra becomes ruler.	6. What did Samudra accomplish during his reign?
	7. What was the significance of Chandra Gupta II's military victories?
A.D. 375 Chandra Gupta II becomes king.	8. What peaceful means did he use to strengthen his empire?

B. *Making Inferences* Explain how the terms **Tamil, matriarchal,** and **patriarchal** relate to daily life in India.

_____

_____

_____

India and China Establish Empires **51**

Name _____ Date _____

GUIDED READING *Trade Spreads Indian Religions and Culture*

A. *Analyzing Issues* As you read about the ways that Indian culture changed and expanded between about 200 B.C. and A.D. 300, fill out the chart by writing notes in the appropriate spaces.

Changes in Religious Thought	
1. Note how Buddhism changed and identify two effects of this change.	
2. Note how Hinduism changed and identify two effects of this change.	

Expansion of Culture	
3. Note at least two examples of the flowering of literature and performing arts.	
4. Note at least two examples of the flowering of science and mathematics.	

Expansion of Trade and Commerce	
5. Note how development of the Silk Roads and increased sea trade contributed to the expansion of Indian commerce.	
6. Note two effects of the expansion of Indian trade.	

B. *Making Inferences* On the back of this paper, identify **Kalidasa** and **Mahayana.** Explain the importance of each to the spread of Indian culture.

Name _____ Date _____

GUIDED READING *Han Emperors in China*

A. *Summarizing* As you read about the Han Dynasty, take notes to fill in the charts.

Ruler	Objectives	How objectives were accomplished
1. Liu Bang	• Destroy rivals' power • Win popular support	
2. Empress Lü	• Keep control of throne	
3. Wudi	• Expand Chinese Empire • Appoint qualified people to government jobs	
4. Wang Mang	• Restore order and bring the country under control	

B. *Analyzing Causes and Recognizing Effects* Use information from Section 3 to identify some results of each situation or event.

Situation or Event	Result(s)
5. Paper is invented.	
6. Government makes techniques of silk production a closely guarded secret.	
7. Territorial expansion brings people of many cultures under Chinese rule.	
8. Gap between rich and poor increases.	

C. *Clarifying* On the back of this paper, define the following terms and explain how they relate to the Han Dynasty.

centralized government   **civil service**   **monopoly**   **assimilation**

Name _____   Date _____

A. Matching Match the description in the second column with the term or name in the first column. Write the appropriate letter next to the word.

____ 1. Mauryan Empire

____ 2. Asoka

____ 3. Gupta Empire

____ 4. Han Dynasty

____ 5. centralized government

____ 6. assimiliation

____ 7. monopoly

____ 8. Tamil

a. empire that oversaw a great flowering of Indian civilization

b. process of making conquered people part of the prevailing culture

c. Indian king who promoted religious toleration

d. empire that helped unify Chinese culture

e. language and people of southern India

f. system in which a central authority controls the running of the state

g. exclusive control by one group over the production and distribution of certain goods

h. empire that united north India politically for the first time

B. Completion Select the term or name that best completes the sentence.

| religious toleration | matriarchal | Theravada | Silk Roads |
| patriarchial | Mahayana | Kalidasa | civil service |

1. Caravan trails that crossed Asia carrying Chinese silk to the West were called the _____.

2. In ancient China, _____ jobs were government jobs that civilians obtained by taking examinations.

3. In ancient India, Buddhists who adhered to the Buddha's strict, original teachings belonged to the _____.

4. One of the greatest writers of ancient India was _____.

5. Most Indian families were _____, which means headed by the eldest male.

6. Some Tamil families were _____, or headed by the mother rather than the father.

C. Writing Use each of the following terms correctly in a brief travelogue describing ancient Indian art.

stupas   Brahma   Vishnu   Shiva

Name _____ Date _____

SKILLBUILDER PRACTICE *Determining Main Ideas*

*A main idea is a statement that summarizes the main point of a speech, an article,
a section of a book, or a paragraph. Sometimes main ideas are stated clearly.
Other times readers must figure out the main idea by studying the entire passage.
Read the two excerpts below and write the main idea on the line that follows.
(See Skillbuilder Handbook.)*

India and China Establish Empires

Asoka became king of the Mauryan Empire in India in 269 B.C. At first, he followed
Kautilya's philosophy of waging war to expand his power. He led a long campaign against his
neighbors to the southeast in the state of Kalinga. During this bloody war, 100,000 soldiers
were slain and even more civilians perished. Although victorious, Asoka felt sorrow over the
slaughter at Kalinga. As a result, he studied Buddhism and decide to rule by Buddha's
teaching of nonviolence and "peace to all beings." Throughout the empire, Asoka erected
huge stone pillars inscribed with his new policies. Some edicts guaranteed that Asoka would
treat his subjects fairly and humanely. Others preached nonviolence and acceptance of people who held different beliefs.

1. Main Idea: _____

_____

When Emperor Liu Bang of China died in 195 B.C., his young son became emperor, but in
name only. The real ruler was the boy's mother, Empress Lü. Although Lü had not been Liu
Bang's only wife, she had powerful friends at court who helped her seize power. The empress
outlived her son and retained control of the throne by naming first one infant and then
another as emperor. Because the infants were too young to rule, she remained in control.
When Empress Lü died in 180 B.C., people who remained loyal to Liu Bang's family, rather
than to Lü's family, came back into power. They rid the palace of the old empress's relatives
by executing them. Such palace plots occurred often during the Han Dynasty.

2. Main Idea: _____

_____

Name _____   Date _____

CHAPTER
7

Section 3

GEOGRAPHY APPLICATION: HUMAN–ENVIRONMENT INTERACTION
The Great Wall of China

Directions: Read the paragraphs below and study the map carefully. Then answer the questions that follow.

Beginning in the fourth century B.C., local rulers in China began building a dirt-and-rubble-filled stone wall to protect their lands against raids from outsiders. The Zhou, Qin, and Han dynasties built the majority of the wall.

However, after the Han Dynasty, much of the wall was allowed to decay for nearly 1,500 years. Finally, during the Ming Dynasty of A.D. 1368–1644, wide-scale restoration on the wall began on sections along the once nearly 4,600 mile structure. However, the section of the wall northeast of Beijing had deteriorated so badly that it was abandoned, and a new section of the wall was constructed almost straight east of Beijing. As a result, today the wall ends at Shanhaiguan, a city on the Bo Hai gulf. Most of the Great Wall depicted in modern photographs consists of relatively short rebuilt sections around Beijing in which improved construction methods were used.

The Great Wall has been the subject of many myths and misconceptions. One misconception is that the entire wall is wide enough that six horse riders moving side by side could have ridden it. But the wall is that wide only in a few areas. Also, the passageways to the top of the wall through the watch towers (there are nearly 25,000 of them along the wall) are too narrow for horses to pass through. Second, there is popular belief that the wall is visible from the moon. It is not, though some sections of the wall have been viewed by astronauts orbiting the earth. The entire wall cannot be seen because over the centuries large sections of it have been reduced to piles of mud. Other sections have become so overgrown with vegetation that they have blended in with natural terrain.

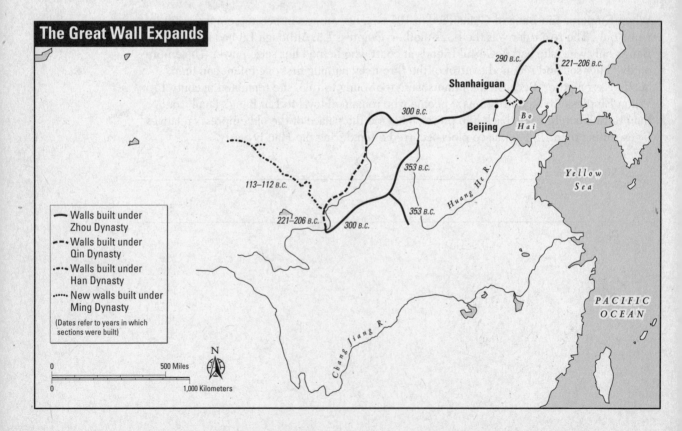

The Great Wall Expands

Legend:
— Walls built under Zhou Dynasty
-·- Walls built under Qin Dynasty
··- Walls built under Han Dynasty
···· New walls built under Ming Dynasty
(Dates refer to years in which sections were built)

290 B.C.
221–206 B.C.
Shanhaiguan
300 B.C.
Beijing
Bo Hai
353 B.C.
113–112 B.C.
Huang He R.
Yellow Sea
221–206 B.C.
300 B.C.
353 B.C.
Chang Jiang R.
PACIFIC OCEAN

0   500 Miles
0   1,000 Kilometers

N

Interpreting Text and Visuals

1. What do the four kinds of lines that depict the Great Wall refer to? _____

2. What do the dates next to nearly all sections of the wall show? _____

   _____

3. What very short section of the wall is not dated? _____

   What does the lack of dates indicate? _____

   _____

4. Which dates fall within the Zhou Dynasty? _____

   Which dates fall within the Qin Dynasty? _____

   Which dates fall within the Han Dynasty? _____

5. What was the Han Dynasty's particular contribution to the Great Wall construction? _____

   _____

6. Today a section of the Great Wall is referred to as the Interior Great Wall. Find it on the map
   and account for that description. _____

   _____

   _____

   Which are older—sections of the Interior or Exterior Great Wall? _____

7. How does the easternmost section of the Great Wall as it is seen today differ from the wall as
   seen in 200 B.C.? _____

   _____

   _____

   _____

Name _____ Date _____

PRIMARY SOURCE *from Arthasastra*
by Kautilya

*Kautilya, Chandragupta Maurya's adviser, wrote a practical guide to politics
called the* Arthasastra. *As you read this passage from Chapter 20 of the handbook, think about what Kautilya recommends a ruler should do to insure his
personal safety.*

The ruler should employ as his security staff only such persons as have noble and proven ancestry and are closely related to him and are well trained and loyal. No foreigners, or anonymous persons, or persons with clouded antecedents are to be employed as security staff for the ruler.

In a securely guarded chamber, the chief should supervise the ruler's food arrangements.

Special precautions are to be taken against contaminated and poisoned food. The following reveal poison: rice sending out deep blue vapour; unnaturally coloured and artificially dried-up and hard vegetables; unusually bright and dull vessels; foamy vessels; streaky soups, milk and liquor; white streaked honey; strange-tempered food; carpets and curtains stained with dark spots and threadbare; polishless and lustreless metallic vessels and gems.

The poisoner reveals himself by parched and dry mouth, hesitating talk, perspiration, tremour, yawning, evasive demeanour and nervous behaviour. Experts in poison detection should be in attendance on the ruler. The physicians attending the ruler should satisfy themselves personally as to the purity of the drugs which they administer to the ruler. The same precaution is indicated for liquor and beverages which the ruler uses. Scrupulous cleanliness should be insisted on in persons in charge of the ruler's dress and toilet requisites. This should be ensured by seals. . . .

In any entertainment meant for the amusement of the ruler, the actors should not use weapons, fire and poison. Musical instruments and accoutrements for horses, elephants and vehicles should be secured in the palace.

The ruler should mount beasts and vehicles only after the traditional rider or driver has done so. If he has to travel in a boat, the pilot should be trust-worthy and the boat itself secured to another boat. There should be a proper convoy on land or water guarding the ruler. He should swim only in rivers which are free of larger fishes and crocodiles and hunt in forests free from snakes, man-eaters and brigands.

He should give private audience only attended by his security guards. He should receive foreign ambassadors in his full ministerial council. While reviewing his militia, the ruler should also attend in full battle uniform and be on horseback or on the back of an elephant. When he enters or exits from the capital city, the path of the ruler should be guarded by staffed officers and cleared of armed men, mendicants and the suspicious. He should attend public performances, festivals, processions or religious gatherings accompanied by trained bodyguards. The ruler should guard his own person with the same care with which he secures the safety of those around him through espionage arrangements.

from William H. McNeill and Jean W. Sedlar, eds., *Classical India* (New York: Oxford University Press, 1969), 20–36. Reprinted in Peter N. Stearns, ed., *Documents in World History*, Vol. 1 (New York: HarperCollins Publishers, 1988), 64.

Activity Options

1. *Clarifying* Write a list of safety tips based on the *Arthasastra*. Then discuss with classmates which of these tips might be of use to modern politicians.
2. *Drawing Conclusions* Draw an illustration that might be used in this manual.

PRIMARY SOURCE *from the* Purānas

A new collection of popular religious literature, the Purānas, emerged as Hinduism changed and became a more personal religion. The following text, which is written in the form of a dialogue between a teacher and his student, describes characteristics of those who worship Vishnu, one of the three most important gods of Hinduism. According to the Purānas, how does a person who worships Vishnu behave?

Praise of Vishnu's Worshipers

"Tell me, master, how am I to distinguish the worshipper of Hari [Vishnu], who is the protector of all beings?" Yama replied: "You are to consider the worshipper of Vishnu him who never deviates from the duties prescribed to his caste; who looks with equal indifference upon friend or enemy; who takes nothing, nor injures any being. Know that person of unblemished mind to be a worshipper of Vishnu. Know him to be a devout worshipper of Hari, who has placed Janārdana [Vishnu] in his pure mind, which has been freed from fascination, and whose soul is undefiled by the soil of the Kali age [the present evil age of humanity]. Know that excellent man to be a worshipper of Vishnu, who, looking upon gold in secret, holds that which is another's wealth but as grass, and devotes all his thoughts to the lord. Pure is he as a mountain of clear crystal: for how can Vishnu abide in the hearts of men with malice, and envy, and other evil passions? The flowing heat of fire abides not in a cluster of the cooling rays of the moon. He who lives pure in thought, free from malice, contented, leading a holy life, feeling tenderness for all creatures, speaking wisely and kindly, humble and sincere, has Vāsudeva [Vishnu] ever present in his heart.

As the young Sāla-tree, by its beauty, declares the excellence of the juices which it has imbibed from the earth, so, when the eternal has taken up his abode in the bosom of any one, that man is lovely amidst the beings of this world.

Depart quickly from those men whose sins have been dispersed by moral and spiritual merit, whose minds are daily dedicated to the imperceptible deity, and who are exempt from pride, uncharitableness, and malice.

In the heart in which the divine Hari, who is without beginning or end, abides, armed with a sword, a shell, and a mace, sin cannot remain; for it cannot coexist with that which destroys it: as darkness cannot continue in the world, when the sun is shining. The eternal makes not his abode in the heart of that man who covets another's wealth, who injures living creatures, who speaks harshness and untruth, who is proud of his iniquity, and whose mind is evil. Janārdana occupies not his thoughts who envies another's prosperity, who calumniates [makes false statements about] the virtuous, who never sacrifices, nor bestows gifts upon the pious, who is blinded by the property of darkness.

That vile wretch is no worshipper of Vishnu, who, through avarice, is unkind to his nearest friends and relations, to his wife, children, parents, and dependents. The brute-like man whose thoughts are evil, who is addicted to unrighteous acts, who ever seeks the society of the wicked, and suffers no day to pass without the perpetration of crime, is no worshipper of Vāsudeva.

from H.H. Wilson, *The Vishnu Purana* (London: Trübner, 1864), 76–78. Reprinted in Louis Renou, ed., *Hinduism* (New York: George Braziller, 1962), 171–172.

Discussion Questions

1. ***Determining Main Ideas*** According to Yama, what kind of person worships Vishnu?
2. ***Drawing Conclusions*** What kind of person does not worship Vishnu?
3. ***Making Inferences*** How does this selection reflect the changes that took place in Hinduism between the Maurya and Gupta empires?

PRIMARY SOURCE *from Lessons for Women*
by Ban Zhao

Chinese scholar Ban Zhao (A.D. 45?–120?) served as the unofficial imperial histori-an to Emperor Ho and taught history, classical writing, astronomy, and math to Empress Teng and her ladies-in-waiting. She wrote Lessons for Women, *from which this excerpt is taken, to advise first-century Chinese women on how to behave properly. According to Ban Zhao, what was a woman's role?*

Introduction

I, the unworthy writer, am unsophisticated, unen-lightened, and by nature unintelligent, but I am fortunate both to have received not a little favor from my scholarly father, and to have had a (cul-tured) mother and instructresses upon whom to rely for a literary education as well as for training in good manners. More than forty years have passed since at the age of fourteen I took up the dustpan and the broom in the Ts'ao family. During this time with trembling heart I feared constantly that I might disgrace my parents, and that I might multi-ply difficulties for both the women and the men (of my husband's family). Day and night I was dis-tressed in heart, (but) I labored without confessing weariness. Now and hereafter, however, I know how to escape (from such fears).

Being careless, and by nature stupid, I taught and trained (my children) without system. Consequently I fear that my son Ku may bring disgrace upon the Imperial Dynasty by whose Holy Grace he has unprecedentedly received the extraordinary privi-lege of wearing the Gold and the Purple, a privi-lege for the attainment of which (by my son, I) a humble subject never even hoped. Nevertheless, now that he is a man and able to plan his own life, I need not again have concern for him. But I do grieve that you, my daughters, just now at the age for marriage, have not at this time had gradual training and advice; that you still have not learned the proper customs for married women. I fear that by failure in good manners in other families you will humiliate both your ancestors and your clan. I am now seriously ill, life is uncertain. As I have thought of you all in so untrained a state, I have been uneasy many a time for you. At hours of leisure I have composed in seven chapters these instructions under the title, "Lessons for Women." In order that you may have something wherewith to benefit your persons, I wish every one of you, my daughters, each to write out a copy for yourself.

From this time on every one of you strive to prac-tise these (lessons).

Chapter I
Humility

On the third day after the birth of a girl the ancients observed three customs: (first) to place the baby below the bed; (second) to give her a potsherd [piece of broken pottery] with which to play; and (third) to announce her birth to her ancestors by an offering. Now to lay the baby below the bed plainly indicated that she is lowly and weak, and should regard it as her primary duty to humble herself before others. To give her potsherds with which to play indubitably [without doubt] signified that she should practise labor and consider it her primary duty to be industrious. To announce her birth before her ancestors clearly meant that she ought to esteem as her primary duty the continuation of the observance of worship in the home.

These three ancient customs epitomize a woman's ordinary way of life and the teachings of the tradi-tional ceremonial rites and regulations. Let a woman modestly yield to others; let her respect others; let her put others first, herself last. Should she do something good, let her not mention it; should she do something bad, let her not deny it. Let her bear disgrace; let her even endure when others speak or do evil to her. Always let her seem to tremble and to fear. (When a woman follows such maxims as these,) then she may be said to humble herself before others.

Let a woman retire late to bed, but rise early to duties; let her not dread tasks by day or by night. Let her not refuse to perform domestic duties whether easy or difficult. That which must be done, let her finish completely, tidily, and systematically. (When a woman follows such rules as these,) then she may be said to be industrious.

Let a woman be correct in manner and upright in character in order to serve her husband. Let her live in purity and quietness (of spirit), and attend to her own affairs. Let her love not gossip and silly laughter. Let her cleanse and purify and arrange in order the wine and the food for the offerings to the ancestors. (When a woman observes such principles as these,) then she may be said to continue ancestral worship.

No woman who observes these three (fundamentals of life) has ever had a bad reputation or has fallen into disgrace. If a woman fail to observe them, how can her name be honored; how can she but bring disgrace upon herself?

Chapter IV
Womanly Qualifications

A woman (ought to) have four qualifications: (1) womanly virtue; (2) womanly words; (3) womanly bearing; and (4) womanly work. Now what is called womanly virtue need not be brilliant ability, exceptionally different from others. Womanly words need be neither clever in debate nor keen in conversation. Womanly appearance requires neither a pretty nor a perfect face and form. Womanly work need not be work done more skillfully than that of others.

To guard carefully her chastity; to control circumspectly her behavior; in every motion to exhibit modesty; and to model each act on the best usage, this is womanly virtue.

To choose her words with care; to avoid vulgar language; to speak at appropriate times; and not to weary others (with much conversation), may be called the characteristics of womanly words.

To wash and scrub filth away; to keep clothes and ornaments fresh and clean; to wash the head and bathe the body regularly, and to keep the person free from disgraceful filth, may be called the characteristics of womanly bearing.

With whole-hearted devotion to sew and to weave; to love not gossip and silly laughter; in cleanliness and order (to prepare) the wine and food for serving guests, may be called the characteristics of womanly work.

These four qualifications characterize the greatest virtue of a woman. No woman can afford to be without them. In fact they are very easy to possess if a woman only treasure them in her heart. The ancients had a saying: "Is Love afar off? If I desire love, then love is at hand!" So can it be said of these qualifications.

from Nancy Lee Swann, *Pan Chao: Foremost Woman Scholar of China* (New York: The Century Co., 1932), 82–87. Reprinted in Peter N. Stearns, ed., *Documents in World History*, Vol. 1 (New York: Harper Collins Publishers, 1988), 52–55.

Discussion Questions

1. *Determining Main Ideas* How did Ban Zhao teach Chinese women to behave?
2. *Drawing Conclusions* According to Ban Zhao, what would happen to women who did not follow her "lessons"?
3. *Making Inferences* Would Ban Zhao's lessons be apt for American women today? Why or why not?

CHAPTER 7

Section 1

LITERATURE SELECTION *from the Panchatantra*
by Vishmusharmam

According to tradition, a Brahman named Vishmusharmam was given six months to teach the art of statecraft to two spoiled young princes. Vishmusharmam wrote a series of 87 witty stories to help him instruct the princes. Known as the Panchatantra or Five Books, these stories were written sometime between 200 B.C. and A.D. 500. What moral lesson does the following story, "The Lion-Makers," teach?

The Lion-Makers

In a certain town were four Brahmans who lived in friendship. Three of them had reached the far shore of all scholarship, but lacked sense. The other found scholarship distasteful; he had nothing but sense.

One day they met for consultation. "What is the use of attainments," said they, "if one does not travel, win the favor of kings, and acquire money? Whatever we do, let us all travel."

But when they had gone a little way, the eldest of them said: "One of us, the fourth, is a dullard, having nothing but sense. Now nobody gains the favorable attention of kings by simple sense without scholarship. Therefore we will not share our earnings with him. Let him turn back and go home."

Then the second said: "My intelligent friend, you lack scholarship. Please go home." But the third said: "No, no. This is no way to behave. For we have played together since we were little boys. Come along, my noble friend. You shall have a share of the money we earn."

With this agreement they continued their journey, and in a forest they found the bones of a dead lion. Thereupon one of them said: "A good opportunity to test the ripeness of our scholarship. Here lies some kind of creature, dead. Let us bring it to life by means of the scholarship we have honestly won."

Then the first said: "I know how to assemble the skeleton." The second said: "I can supply skin, flesh, and blood." The third said: "I can give it life."

So the first assembled the skeleton, the second provided skin, flesh, and blood. But while the third was intent on giving the breath of life, the man of sense advised against it, remarking: "This is a lion. If you bring him to life, he will kill every one of us."

"You simpleton!" said the other, "it is not I who will reduce scholarship to a nullity." "In that case," came the reply, "wait a moment, while I climb this convenient tree."

When this had been done, the lion was brought to life, rose up, and killed all three. But the man of sense, after the lion had gone elsewhere, climbed down and went home.

"And that is why I say:
Scholarship is less than sense;
Therefore seek intelligence:
Senseless scholars in their pride
Made a lion; then they died."

from Arthur W. Ryder, trans., *The Panchatantra* (Chicago: University of Chicago Press). Reprinted in Lin Yutang, ed., *The Wisdom of China and India* (New York: Random House, 1942), 276–277.

Discussion Questions
Determining Main Ideas
1. Why did the four Brahmans decide to travel?
2. Why did the man of sense advise against bringing the lion back to life?
3. ***Categorizing*** The stories in the *Panchatantra* are grouped into five categories—Loss of Friends, Winning of Friends, Crows and Owls (international relations), Loss of Gains, and Ill-Considered Action. In which category would you place "The Lion-Makers"? Why?

CHAPTER
7
Section 2

LITERATURE SELECTION *from Shakuntala*
by **Kalidasa**

Kalidasa was a poet and playwright who probably lived in the fifth century in India. His most famous play, Shakuntala, tells the story of a young girl who marries King Dushyanta. Because of an enemy's curse, the king forgets his wife and will only recognize her again by means of a ring that he gave to her. Unfortunately, Shakuntala drops the ring in the Ganges River while she is worshiping. Who finds the ring in this scene from Act VI?

Act VI
Separation from Shakuntala

Scene I.—In the street before the Palace
(Enter the chief of police, two policemen, and a man with his hands bound behind his back.)

THE TWO POLICEMEN (striking the man): Now, pickpocket, tell us where you found this ring. It is the king's ring, with letters engraved on it, and it has a magnificent great gem.

FISHERMAN (showing fright): Be merciful, kind gentlemen. I am not guilty of such a crime.

FIRST POLICEMAN: No, I suppose the king thought you were a pious Brahman, and made you a present of it.

FISHERMAN: Listen, please. I am a fisherman, and I live on the Ganges, at the spot where Indra came down.

SECOND POLICEMAN: You thief, we didn't ask for your address or your social position.

CHIEF: Let him tell a straight story, Suchaka. Don't interrupt.

THE TWO POLICEMEN: Yes, chief. Talk, man, talk.

FISHERMAN: I support my family with things you catch fish with—nets, you know, and hooks, and things.

CHIEF (laughing): You have a sweet trade.

FISHERMAN: Don't say that, master.

You can't give up a lowdown trade
That your ancestors began;
A butcher butchers things, and yet
He's the tenderest-hearted man.

CHIEF: Go on. Go on.

FISHERMAN: Well, one day I was cutting up a carp. In its maw I see this ring with the magnificent great gem. And then I was just trying to sell it here when you kind gentlemen grabbed me.

"Don't kill a man without any reason, master."

That is the only way I got it. Now kill me, or find fault with me.

CHIEF (smelling the ring): There is no doubt about it, Januka. It has been in a fish's maw. It has the real perfume of raw meat. Now we have to find out how he got it. We must go to the palace.

THE TWO POLICEMEN (to the fisherman): Move on, you cutpurse, move on. (They walk about.)

CHIEF: Suchaka, wait here at the big gate until I come out of the palace. And don't get careless.

THE TWO POLICEMEN: Go in, chief. I hope the king will be nice to you.

CHIEF: Good-bye. (Exit.)

SUCHAKA: Januka, the chief is taking his time.

JANUKA: You can't just drop in on a king.

SUCHAKA: Januka, my fingers are itching (indicating the fisherman) to kill this cutpurse.

FISHERMAN: Don't kill a man without any reason, master.

JANUKA (looking ahead): There is the chief, with a written order from the king. (To the fisherman.) Now you will see your family, or else you will feed the crows and jackals. (Enter the chief.)

CHIEF: Quick! Quick! (He breaks off.)

FISHERMAN: Oh, oh! I'm a dead man. (He shows dejection.)

CHIEF: Release him, you. Release the fishnet fellow. It is all right, his getting the ring. Our king told me so himself.

SUCHAKA: All right, chief. He is a dead man come back to life. (He releases the fisherman.)

FISHERMAN (bowing low to the chief): Master, I owe you my life. (He falls at his feet.)

CHIEF: Get up, get up! Here is a reward that the king was kind enough to give you. It is worth as much as the ring. Take it. (He hands the fisherman a bracelet.)

FISHERMAN (joyfully taking it): Much obliged.

JANUKA: He is much obliged to the king. Just as if he had been taken from the stake and put on an elephant's back.

SUCHAKA: Chief, the reward shows that the king thought a lot of the ring. The gem must be worth something.

CHIEF: No, it wasn't the fine gem that pleased the king. It was this way.

THE TWO POLICEMEN: Well?

CHIEF: I think, when the king saw it, he remembered somebody he loves. You know how dignified he is usually. But as soon as he saw it, he broke down for a moment.

SUCHAKA: You have done the king a good turn, chief.

JANUKA: All for the sake of this fish-killer, it seems to me. (He looks enviously at the fisherman.)

FISHERMAN: Take half of it, masters, to pay for something to drink.

JANUKA: Fisherman, you are the biggest and best friend I've got. The first thing we want, is all the brandy we can hold. Let's go where they keep it. (*Exeunt omnes.*)

from Arthur W. Ryder, trans., *Shakuntala and Other Writings by Kalidasa,* (New York: E. P. Dutton & Co., Inc., 1959), 63–65.

Activity Options

1. *Summarizing* With a small group of classmates, rehearse and then perform this scene.
2. *Synthesizing* As either Suchaka or Januka, write up the police report about this incident. Share your report with classmates.

CHAPTER 7

Section 1

HISTORYMAKERS Chandra Gupta II
"Sun of Prowess"

"The inhabitants are rich and prosperous, and vie with each other in the practice of benevolence and righteousness."—Faxian, on India under Chandra Gupta II

The Gupta Empire began in A.D. 320 and marked the start of India's golden age. One historian, looking at the chaos seen in the Roman world and China at the same time, said it was "possibly the happiest and most civilized region in the world." Samudra Gupta, his son Chandra Gupta II, and his grandson Kumara Gupta each ruled India for about 40 years. Chandra Gupta II helped the empire flourish. A skillful warrior, he expanded India until it reached its greatest extent. During his reign, he also saw many people complete great works of drama, poetry, and art, while scholars reached new heights in learning.

Chandra Gupta II came to the throne in 375. The new emperor proved that he had his father's military ability. When he took the throne, the Gupta Empire stretched along the north of India from the mouth of the Ganges River at the Bay of Bengal to central India. In just over a decade, Chandra Gupta had conquered the land of the Sakas to the west. These victories gave the empire the important cities of Gujarat and Ujjain. Gujarat was one of several important ports on the Arabian Sea. By taking them, the Gupta Empire now had access to the rich trade of Southwest Asia and points west. Trade goods moved north from these ports to Ujjain. However, this ancient city was more than just an important trading center. It was one of the seven sacred cities of Hinduism.

With his conquests Chandra Gupta added a name—Vikramaditya, or "Sun of Prowess." The name was linked to a legendary ruler of Ujjain who had fought the Sakas centuries before. Afterward, many stories about the great achievements of Vikramaditya were still remembered in northern India. Along with taking this legendary name, Chandra Gupta also tried to enhance his standing using images. The coins of his reign show him enjoying the favorite pastime of Indian kings—fighting lions single-handedly.

However, the emperor did not need such heavy-handed public relations work. His rule was a glorious time for India. The empire was at peace. The imperial treasury was full and growing richer with increased trade. Royal officials received a fixed salary, which cut down on the chance that they would seek bribes.

Faxian, a traveler from China who spent several years in the emperor's lands, was impressed by how content the people were. Under the previous Maurya Empire, secret police had roamed the land, keeping a watchful eye on the people. Under Chandra Gupta, people were largely left alone. This was even true in the realm of religion. Although the emperor was a devout Hindu, Buddhists were not bothered.

Chandra Gupta also supported the arts. The emperor himself backed Kalidasa, the leading playwright of India who produced plays for the imperial court each year. Fables and fairy tales from the period later traveled to other lands and influenced such works as *A Thousand and One Nights*. In addition, poets wrote intricate and complex poems that showed great creativity. One person actually wrote one that had a certain meaning when read left to right and another when read right to left.

In science the Gupta Age saw remarkable achievements. Astronomers concluded that the earth was round and that it rotated. Mathematicians worked with negative numbers and quadratic equations. They also created two mathematical concepts that would later spread around the world: the idea of zero and the use of what are now called Arabic numbers. With all the achievements of his time, Chandra Gupta II was truly a "Sun of Prowess."

Questions

1. ***Making Inferences*** Why would it help the empire to have only a few rulers who ruled for long periods of time?

2. ***Analyzing Causes and Recognizing Effects*** How did Chandra Gupta's conquests help his empire?

3. ***Analyzing Primary and Secondary Sources*** Why would a ruler like Chandra Gupta change his name and issue coins showing him fighting lions?

CHAPTER **7**

Section 3

HISTORYMAKERS Wudi

A Long Reign of Change

"[Wudi's] reign was the high point of Han power, prestige, and morale."
—historian Charles Hucker

The Han emperor Wudi took the throne in 141 B.C. as a young man full of energy, confidence, and plans. He died 54 years later, having achieved one of the longest rules in Chinese history. He is known for far more than the length of his reign, however. Wudi made profound changes on Chinese society—changes that had an impact long after his death.

Wudi was an unlikely emperor. He was the eleventh son of emperor Chingdi and had many brothers with better claims to the throne. However, a group of court officials convinced Chingdi to name the boy as his successor. Before Wudi there had been five Han emperors, all of whom had ruled cautiously. Wudi took a different approach.

First, he moved to break the power of the local nobles. He began by draining their wealth with heavy financial burdens. Nobles were required, for instance, to give certain gifts to the emperor to show their loyalty. But those gifts could only be purchased from the royal treasury at extremely high prices. The emperor also took a direct approach, seizing the land of many lords. Those who escaped these two actions faced a third. Wudi ordered that, upon the death of a land owner, all his property was to be divided equally among all his sons. With this, large estates were broken up by the passing of each generation.

The emperor acted against merchants and traders as well. Under previous rulers, trade had thrived. Many business owners had built huge fortunes, especially in the trade of iron, salt, liquor, and grain. Wudi put the imperial state in charge of all these goods. He then taxed these products heavily to increase the flow of funds into the royal treasury.

The emperor also increased his hold on government officials. He created a new system that ignored the nobles who had previously run the government. Instead, he used scholars trained in the ideas of Confucius. He formed schools throughout the empire to teach these ideas. Now, through a system of recommendations, able men could rise to high office.

Wudi also adopted Confucianism as the state religion. This move had a profound impact on later Chinese society. The Confucian emphasis on acting out important rituals became a central part of Chinese government and religion.

Finally, Wudi worked to expand Han China. For 18 years his soldiers fought against the Xiongnu nomads to the north. The emperor followed up his victories by sending Chinese settlers to conquered areas. He sent about 700,000 people to live in colonies that extended Han China into central Asia.

The emperor also made arrangements with the rulers there. They were forced to admit the superiority of China and pay tribute. They were also instructed to send a son to the Chinese court. The sons were educated in Chinese ideas and were, in effect, hostages that ensured that their fathers would cooperate. With these steps, Wudi established a pattern of relations with foreign powers that the Chinese followed for many future centuries.

Wudi expanded Han influence to other areas as well. The Chinese took much of Korea and moved into what is now Vietnam. Along with political control, the Han brought in their culture. While Korea and Vietnam modified Chinese ideas and practices, they were still strongly influenced by them.

Late in his reign, Wudi's policies backfired. Heavy spending on wars—and on the luxuries of his lifestyle—reduced the treasury. For three generations Han emperors had built a huge surplus of money. Wudi spent it all. His aggressive tax and business policies did more than break the power of the merchants. They also slowed the economy.

The aging emperor had other troubles as well. In 91 B.C., after 50 years of rule, he was shocked to hear that the son he had named to follow him was accused of witchcraft against him. Wudi died four years later.

Questions

1. *Identifying Problems and Solutions* How did Wudi reduce the power of nobles?
2. *Drawing Conclusions* Do you think Wudi's economic policies were wise? Why or why not?
3. *Developing Historical Perspective* Which of Wudi's actions do you think had the most lasting impact? Explain.

Name _____ Date _____

CONNECTIONS ACROSS TIME AND CULTURES
Governing an Empire

THEMATIC CONNECTION:
POWER AND AUTHORITY

One of the main themes of this book is empire building. In this chapter, you learned about ancient empires in India and China. In Chapter 6, you learned about the Roman Empire. What patterns emerge as you compare how these empires dealt with problems of governing large areas? To find out, answer the questions that follow.

Problem	Roman Empire	Mauryan Empire	Han Empire
1. What is the best way to govern an empire?	bureaucracy of plebeians and former slaves		
2. How can conquered peoples be made part of the empire?	tolerate local cultures, give government offices to conquered people, use army service to spread Roman culture to frontier peoples		
3. How should farmers be treated?	slave labor on large estates make small farmers poor		
4. How should traders be treated?	build roads, use navy power to protect merchant ships		

5. How does the United States encourage immigrants to become part of the nation? _____

_____

_____

6. What lessons do you think modern-day leaders might learn by studying the

patterns of ancient empires? _____

_____

_____

CHAPTER
7
Section 1

RETEACHING ACTIVITY *India's First Empires*

Clarifying
Write T in the blank if the statement is true. If the statement is false, write F in the blank and then write the corrected statement on the line below it.

_____ 1. Chandragupta Maurya claimed the throne of the kingdom of Magadha in about 321 B.C., which began the Gupta Empire.

_____

_____ 2. When Chandragupta defeated Seleucus I, the land gains united north India politically for the first time in history.

_____

_____ 3. Kautilya, one of Chandragupta's advisers, wrote a ruler's handbook called the *Vedas*.

_____

_____ 4. Chandragupta's grandson Asoka raised the empire to its greatest heights.

_____

_____ 5. Asoka promoted Buddhism and a policy of religious toleration, acceptance of people who held different beliefs.

_____

_____ 6. Asoka's policies of toleration and non-violence, as well as the improvements in roads made during his reign, held the empire together after his death.

_____

_____ 7. The Andhra Dynasty arose in central India and dominated the region for many years after Asoka's death.

_____

_____ 8. The people in the three kingdoms of southern India spoke the Tamil language.

_____

_____ 9. India's second empire, the Magadha empire, was ruled by Chandra Gupta.

_____

_____ 10. Most Indian families were patriarchal, headed by the eldest female.

_____

CHAPTER 7 Section 2

RETEACHING ACTIVITY *Trade Spreads Indian Religions and Culture*

Reading Comprehension

Find the name or term in the second column that best matches the description in the first column. Then write the letter of your answer in the blank. Note: Some questions may have more than one answer.

_____ 1. India's two main faiths at 250 B.C.

_____ 2. Followers of the new doctrines of Buddhism, which offered salvation to all and allowed popular worship

_____ 3. Followers of Buddhism's stricter, original teachings

_____ 4. Mounded stone structures built over holy relics

_____ 5. In Hinduism, the god who created the world

_____ 6. In Hinduism, the god who is the preserver of the world

_____ 7. Famous Indian writer who wrote *Shakuntala*

_____ 8. Popular name for Indian movie industry

_____ 9. Mathematical concepts that were invented in India during the flowering of Indian culture that lasted until about A.D. 500

_____ 10. Caravan routes that traders used to transport silk and other goods

_____ 11. Country that exported ivory to India

_____ 12. Increased trade led to the rise of this business in India

A. stupas

B. Theravada sect

C. Kalidasa

D. Buddhism

E. Silk Roads

F. decimal system

G. Brahma

H. Africa

I. Vishnu

J. banking

K. Hinduism

L. Christianity

M. Bollywood

N. Mahayana sect

O. Shiva

P. zero

Name _____ Date _____

Multiple Choice

Choose the best answer for each item. Write the letter of your answer in the blank.

_____ 1. The dynasty that restored unity to China
after Shi Huangdi's government crumbled
was the
   a. Han.
   b. Qin.
   c. Ming.
   d. Zhou.

_____ 2. The first emperor of this dynasty was
   a. Shi Huangdi.
   b. Xiang Yu.
   c. Liu Bang.
   d. Wudi.

_____ 3. A government in which a main authority
controls the running of the state is a
   a. democracy.
   b. oligarchy.
   c. republican government.
   d. centralized government.

_____ 4. Empress Lü retained control of the Han
Dynasty by
   a. holding an election.
   b. marrying the new emperor.
   c. naming a series of infants as emperor.
   d. killing her husband, the emperor.

_____ 5. The "Great Game" refers to
   a. the debate that took place at the Berlin
      Conference.
   b. the contest between Britain and Russia
      over Muslim lands in Central Asia.
   c. theBoer war over South Africa.
   d. the military strategies Russia used to
      protect Afghanistan from Great Britain.

_____ 6. Who is known as the "martial emperor"
because he expanded the Chinese empire
through war?
   a. Wudi
   b. Liu Bang
   c. Xiongnu
   d. Shi Huangdi

_____ 7. Government jobs that Chinese civilians
obtained by taking examinations were
known as
   a. Confucianism.
   b. the Civil Service.
   c. a bureaucracy.
   d. scholar-officials.

_____ 8. A group that has exclusive control over the
production and distribution of certain
goods is called a
   a. dynasty.

Name _____ Date _____

GUIDED READING *Diverse Societies in Africa*

A. *Analyzing Causes and Recognizing Effects* As you read about Africa's diverse societies, fill out the chart.

How did each environmental feature affect the peoples of ancient Africa?

Environmental feature	Effect on Africans
1. Waterfalls and rapids	
2. Sahara and Kalahari deserts	
3. Mediterranean coastal areas	
4. Tsetse fly	
5. Fertile land of savannas	

B. *Drawing Conclusions* Take notes to explain how the people in each group adapted to their environment.

Group	Methods of Adaptation
6. San of the Kalahari Desert	
7. Nok people	
8. People of Djenné-Djeno	

C. *Determining Main Ideas* Describe what the societies south of the Sahara had in common. Use the following terms in your description.

extended family   **clan**   **animism**   **griots**

Name _____ Date _____

Drawing Conclusions As you read this case study about the Bantu migrations, take notes to answer the questions below.

Bantu-speaking peoples adapted their skills to new environments they encountered in their migrations southward.	
1. a. How did they change their farming in the rain forests?	2. a. How did they change their techniques for herding in the savannas?
b. Why was the change necessary?	b. Why did they make this change?
3. Some of their adaptations caused them to continue their migrations to new places. Why?	

The migrations of the Bantu-speaking peoples helped to shape the cultures of the African continent.	
4. a. Why did the Bantu-speaking peoples move southward, rather than to the north?	5. a. How did the Bantu speakers relate to the people they did not drive out?
b. What happened to the non-Bantu-speaking hunter-gatherer societies as the newcomers spread south?	b. What were some results of their intermingling?
6. How did the Bantu speakers help unify the various peoples of Africa?	

Name _____ Date _____

GUIDED READING *The Kingdom of Aksum*

A. *Analyzing Causes and Recognizing Effects* As you read about the Kingdom of Aksum, briefly note the causes or effects (depending on which is missing) of each situation.

Causes	Effects
1. Aksum had access to the Red Sea, Blue Nile, and White Nile. →	
2. The port city of Adulis included people from Aksum's trading partners. →	
→	3. The Aksumites created terrace farming, which retained water and prevented erosion.
4. Islamic invaders seized footholds in Africa, destroyed Adulis, and spread the religion of Islam. →	
→	5. Aksum's new geographic location led to its decline as a power.

B. *Clarifying* On the back of this paper, briefly identify **Aksum, Adulis,** and **Ezana.**

Name _____ Date _____

A. *Multiple Choice* Circle the letter before the term or name that best completes the sentence.

1. The religious belief that spirits present in animals, plants, and other natural forces play a role in regulating daily life is called (a) griot (b) animism (c) migration.

2. The availability of fertile land for farming is an example of a (a) pull factor (b) push factor (c) push-pull factor.

3. The chief seaport of Aksum was (a) Adulis (b) Ezana (c) Nok.

4. The oldest known city in Africa south of the Sahara was (a) Aksum (b) Ezana (c) Djenné-Djeno.

5. The African kingdom that became an international trading power, adopted Christianity, and reached its height in the A.D. 300s was (a) Kush (b) Aksum (c) Ezana.

6. In order to farm hilly land, the Askumites constructed steplike ridges called (a) griots (b) savannas (c) terraces.

B. *Evaluating* Write *T* in the blank if the statement is true. If the statement is false, write *F* in the blank and then write the corrected statement on the line below.

_____ 1. The first West African people known to smelt iron were the Djenné-Djeno.

_____

_____ 2. Over the course of about 1,500 years, the Bantu-speaking peoples spread out from a small area south of the Sahara to the tip of Africa.

_____

_____ 3. In ancient Africa, the history and literature of a culture was passed on from generation to generation by storytellers called griots.

_____

_____ 4. A permanent move from one country or region to another is called cultural exchange.

_____

_____ 5. Ezana was a Nok king who led the first Bantu migrations.

_____

C. *Writing* Use the following terms in writing a brief description of Africa's physical geography.

Sahara   Sahel   savanna

Name _____   Date _____

SKILLBUILDER PRACTICE *Identifying Problems*

When you identify problems, you look for challenges a particular people faced at a certain time and how they handled these challenges. As you read, look for problems that are stated directly as well as problems that are implied by the actions people take. Also note that sometimes solutions to one problem result in other problems. Read the passage below and then fill in the chart that follows. (See Skillbuilder Handbook)

Desertification, Deforestation, and Drought Ancient north African people named the area south of the Sahara the *Sahel*, which means "coastline" in Arabic. To these ancient people, the Sahara appeared to be a vast ocean of sand. Since ancient times, the desert has taken over more and more of the Sahel during periods when the rainfall is low.

The people who live in the Sahel support themselves by farming and by herding camels, cattle, and sheep. To cope with the challenge of dry climate and poor soil, farmers practice shifting agriculture. Using this method, farmers prepare a site and grow crops for a year or two. Having exhausted the soil, they leave the farmed land. They move on, clear a new area, and plant their crops. Trees are also cut down for firewood for cooking.

This deforestation, or stripping the land of its trees, damages the environment. Deforestation allows fertile soil to be blown away, leading to soil erosion and drought. Overgrazing of herds also destroys plants and trees and contributes to the problem. More and more of the Sahel becomes desert.

In the mid-1960s and lasting into the 1970s, a severe drought hit the Sahel. Farming in the region ended, and over 200,000 people died of starvation. As the desert spread, many people living in the Sahel fled to the cities. There they lived in huge refugee camps.

During the drought, foreign countries provided food, medicines, and technical aid. Hundreds of miles of trees were planted to protect the soil from blowing away during the dry season and allowing vegetation to grow during the rainy season. In addition to tree planting, technicians from worldwide agencies are teaching the people of the Sahel irrigation and other techniques to help them survive in their harsh environment.

Problems	Solutions	Outcomes

CHAPTER 8

Section 2

GEOGRAPHY APPLICATION: REGION

Desertification and Migration in Africa

Directions: Read the paragraphs below and study the maps carefully. Then answer the questions that follow.

Human migration usually takes thousands of years and can be caused by a variety of factors. One of those factors is environmental change, and it occurred on a large scale on the African continent. The change centered on the northern section of Africa, where the present-day Sahara Desert is located. Before 10,000 B.C., the Sahara region received abundant rainfall, from ten to fifty times as much as it does today. As a result, many groups of people once inhabited this lush and fertile section of Africa.

Then, between 10,000 and 7000 B.C., temperatures rose and rainfall became less frequent, leading to desertification, a drying of the soil. Around 3000 B.C., much of northern Africa became the Sahara Desert.

As the desert slowly expanded, groups of people began to move south toward grassy savannas and north to the Mediterranean fringe, regions that could support human and animal life. This movement sparked a whole set of changes. As people moved, so did their ideas and technology. Iron-making capability, agricultural techniques, and other new ideas rapidly spread across the continent. This climatic change was also a major factor in the Bantu migrations.

The same environmental conditions that began this process are still occurring today. The Sahara desert continues to expand southward, causing many problems in central Africa.

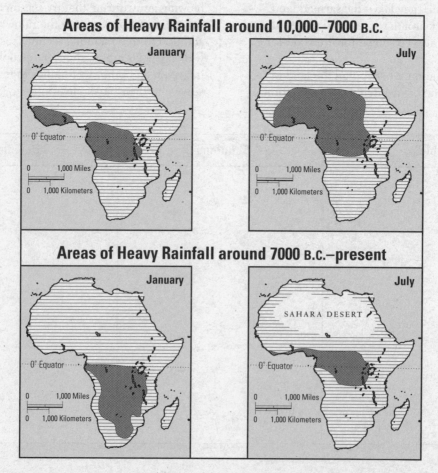

Areas of Heavy Rainfall around 10,000–7000 B.C.

January

July

Areas of Heavy Rainfall around 7000 B.C.–present

January

July

SAHARA DESERT

Interpreting Text and Visuals

1. Where was the African rainfall centered around 10,000–7000 B.C. in the month of July?

   _____

2. Where is the rainfall centered since 7000 B.C. in the month of January? _____

   _____

3. On which two rainfall maps are the areas of rainfall nearly equal? _____

   _____

4. How many miles farther south does rainfall extend in January, 7000 B.C.–present as compared to
   January, 10,000–7000 B.C.? _____

5. In which month did more rain fall during 10,000–7000 B.C.? 7000 B.C.–present? _____

   _____

6. Why did people migrate toward the areas of rainfall?_____

   _____

   _____

7. How does migrating affect the development of technology and ideas in the world? _____

   _____

   _____

   _____

Name _____ Date _____

PRIMARY SOURCE Nok Sculpture

The Nok people lived in what is now northern Nigeria between 500 B.C. and A.D. 200. This terra cotta sculpture is an artifact from the Nok culture. As you study this sculpture, think about what it reveals about the Nok.

Jos Museum, Nigeria/Werner Forman Archive/Art Resource, New York.

Research Options

1. ***Using Research in Writing*** Find out more about the process of making terra cotta sculpture like this one. Then write down your findings to share with the class.

2. ***Making Inferences*** Find pictures of other Nok artifacts. Then work with a small group of classmates to list information that you can learn about the Nok people by studying these artifacts. Discuss your lists with other groups.

Name _____ Date _____

PRIMARY SOURCE *from Natural History*
by Pliny the Elder

During the first century A.D., the Roman emperor Nero sent explorers to find the source of the Nile. Although the explorers were unsuccessful, they did return with information about Meroë, the capital of the powerful kingdom of Kush, during its golden age. This account by Roman historian Pliny the Elder is based on the findings of the Roman exploratory expedition. As you read, look for details that are clearly false or greatly exaggerated.

The persons sent by Nero for the purposes of discovery have reported that . . . from [Napata] to the island of Meroë the distance is three hundred and sixty miles. They also state that the grass in the vicinity of Meroë becomes of a greener and fresher color, and that there is some slight appearance of forests, as also traces of the rhinoceros and elephant. They reported also that the city of Meroë stands at a distance of seventy miles from the first entrance of the island of Meroë, and that close to it is another island, Tadu by name, which forms a harbor facing those who enter the right-hand channel of the river. The buildings in the city, they said, were but few in number, and they stated that a female, whose name was Candace, ruled over the district, that name having passed from queen to queen for many years. They related also that there was a temple of Jupiter Hammon there, held in great veneration, besides smaller shrines erected in honor of him throughout all the country. In addition to these particulars, they were informed that in the days of the Aethiopian dominion, the island of Meroë enjoyed great renown, and that, according to tradition, it was in the habit of maintaining two hundred thousand armed men, and four thousand artisans. The kings of Aethiopia are said even at the present day to be forty-five in number.

The whole of this country has successively had the names of Aetheria, Atlantia, and last of all, Aethiopia, from Aethiops, the son of Vulcan. It is not at all surprising that towards the extremity of this region the men and animals assume a monstrous form, when we consider the changeableness

and volubility of fire, the heat of which is the great agent in imparting various forms and shapes to bodies. Indeed, it is reported that in the interior, on the eastern side, there is a people that have no noses, the whole face presenting a plane surface; that others again are destitute of the upper lip, and others are without tongues. Others again, have the mouth grown together, and being destitute of nostrils, breathe through one passage only, imbibing their drink through it by means of the hollow stalk of the oat, which there grows spontaneously and supplies them with its grain for food. Some of these nations have to employ gestures by nodding the head and moving the limbs, instead of speech. Others again were unacquainted with the use of fire before the time of Ptolemy Lathyrus, king of Egypt.

from John Bostock and H.T. Riley, trans., *The Natural History of Pliny* (Covent Garden, England: Henry G. Bohn). Reprinted in Alvin M. Josephy, ed., *The Horizon History of Africa* (American Heritage, 1971), 77–78.

Discussion Questions

1. ***Determining Main Ideas*** What information about Meroë—its geography, its architecture, its politics, and so on—was included in this account? List at least three facts.
2. ***Distinguishing Fact from Opinions*** Which information included in this account do you think was obviously incorrect? Why?
3. ***Drawing Conclusions*** What do you think the possible consequences of spreading misinformation about Meroë might have been?

Name _____   Date _____

CHAPTER 8

Section 3

PRIMARY SOURCE *from Periplus of the Erythrean Sea*

The Periplus of the Erythrean Sea, *which was written by an unknown Greek in the first century* A.D.., *was a guide for sailors and commercial travelers to the Indian Ocean and the Aden and Persian gulfs. This excerpt from the guide describes Adulis, the chief seaport in Aksum. What goods could you buy in Adulis from traders from around the world?*

Shoppers' Guide to Aksum

Adulis [is] a port established by law, lying at the inner end of a bay that runs in toward the south. Before the harbor lies the so-called Mountain Island, about two hundred stadia seaward from the very head of the bay, with the shores of the mainland close to it on both sides. Ships bound for this port now anchor here because of attacks from the land. They used formerly to anchor at the very head of the bay, by an island called Diodorus, close to the shore, which could be reached on foot from the land; by which means the barbarous natives attacked the island. Opposite Mountain Island, on the mainland twenty stadia from the shore, lies Adulis, a fair-sized village, from which there is a three days' journey to Coloe, an inland town and the first market for ivory. From that place to [Aksum] the city of the people called Auxumites there is a five days' journey more, to that place all the ivory is brought from the country beyond the Nile through the district called Cyeneum [probably modern Sennaar, in the Eastern Sudan], and thence to Adulis. Practically the whole number of elephants and rhinoceros that are killed live in the places inland, although at rare intervals they are hunted on the seacoast even near Adulis.

There are imported into these places, undressed cloth made in Egypt for the Berbers; robes from Arsinoë [modern Suez]; cloaks of poor quality dyed in colors; double-fringed linen mantles; many articles of flint glass, and others of murrhine [probably agate or carnelian], made in Diospolis [probably Thebes]; and brass, which is used for ornament and in cut pieces instead of coin; sheets of soft copper, used for cooking utensils and cut up for bracelets and anklets for the women; iron, which is made into spears used against the elephants and other wild beasts, and in their wars. Besides these, small axes are imported, and adzes and swords; copper drinking-cups, round and large; a little coin for those coming to the market; wine of Laodicea [on the Syrian coast] and Italy, not much; olive oil, not much; for the King, gold and silver plate made after the fashion of the country, and for clothing, military cloaks, and thin coats of skin, of no great value. Likewise from the district of Ariaca [on northwest coast of India around Gulf of Cambay] across this sea, there are imported Indian cloth called monaché [fine quality cotton] and that called sagmotogene [probably tree cotton], and girdles, and coats of skin and mallow-colored cloth, and a few muslins, and colored lac. There are exported from these places ivory, and tortoise-shell and rhinoceros-horn. The most from Egypt is brought to this market [Adulis] from the month of January to September, that is from Tylei to Thoth; but seasonably they put to sea about the month of September.

from Richard Pankhurst, ed., *Travellers in Ethiopia* (Oxford University Press, 1965). Reprinted in Alvin M. Josephy, ed., *The Horizon History of Africa* (American Heritage, 1971), 80.

Activity Options

1. *Recognizing Main Idea* With a group of classmates, role-play Aksumite merchants and merchants from Egypt, Arsinoë, Laodicea, Italy, and Ariaca who trade their wares in Adulis.

2. *Creating a Map* Use a world map to illustrate Aksum's importance as an international trading center. First, mark the site of Adulis (near present-day Massawa) and countries where merchants came from—Egypt, Syria, Italy, and India—with colored push pins. Then link Adulis and the other locations by stringing pieces of colored yarn between the push pins.

CHAPTER
8
Section 3

PRIMARY SOURCE *from A History of the Sudan*
by A. J. Arkell

In about A.D. 350, King Ezana of Aksum launched a military campaign against the kingdom of Kush because the Noba, a nomadic tribe of Kushites, frequently attacked Aksum and its dependencies. Ezana left a record of his victory on a stele, or towering stone pillar. According to this portion of Ezana's record, how did he conquer Kush?

I, 'Ezana, the son of 'Ella 'Amida, a native of Halen, king of Aksum and of Himyar and Raydan and of Saba, and of Salhen, and of Seyamo and of Beja [Blemmyes] and of Kasu [Kush-Meroë], king of kings . . . made war upon Noba, for the peoples had rebelled and had boasted of it . . . "They [the Aksumites] will not cross the river Takkaze [the River Atbara]," said the peoples of Noba. And they were in the habit of attacking the peoples of Mangurto and Khasa and Barya and the blacks and of making war upon the red peoples [citizens of Aksum]. Twice and thrice they had broken their solemn oaths, and had killed their neighbors without mercy, and they had stripped our deputies and messengers whom I sent to enquire into their raids, and had stolen their weapons and belongings. And as I had warned them, and they would not listen but refused to cease from their evil deeds and betook themselves to flight, I made war on them . . . and fought with them on the Takkaze, at the ford of Kemalke. They fled without making a stand, and I pursued them for 23 days, killing some and capturing others . . . I burnt their towns, both those built of bricks and those built of reeds, and my army carried off their food and copper and iron . . . and destroyed the statues in their temples, their granaries, and cotton trees and cast them into the river Seda [Nile]. And I came to Kasu [Kush, where indigenous Meroitic peoples still lived] and fought a battle and captured prisoners at the junction of

the rivers Seda and Takkaze. And the next day I dispatched the army Mahaza, and the army Hara, and Damawa and Falha and Sera up the Seda to raid the country and the cities built of bricks and of reeds. The cities built of brick were 'Alwa [possibly Meroë] and Daro [possibly Kadaro north of Khartoum] . . . and after that I sent the army of Halen and the army of Laken down the Seda against the four towns of the Noba which are made of reeds . . . The towns built of bricks which the Noba had taken were Tabito and Fertoti. And my peoples reached the frontier of the Red Noba [presumably Napata] and they returned in safety, having defeated the Noba and spoiled them by the might of the Lord of Heaven. And I planted a throne in that country at the place where the rivers Seda and Takkaze join. . . .

from A. J. Arkell, *A History of the Sudan* (London: The Athlone Press). Reprinted in *The Horizon History of Africa* (American Heritage, 1971), 80.

Discussion Questions

1. ***Determining Main Ideas*** According to Ezana, why did he make war on the kingdom of Kush?
2. ***Analyzing Causes and Recognizing Effects*** What were the effects of Ezana's war against the Kushites?
3. ***Evaluating Courses of Action*** Do you think Ezana's actions were justified? Why or why not?

Name _____ Date _____

CHAPTER 8

Section 3

LITERATURE SELECTION *from the* Kebra Negast

The **Kebra Negast**, *or the* **Book of the Glory of Kings**, *was written in the early 1300s by Yashaq, a priest of Aksum. The* **Kebra Negast** *traces the legend of the founding of the dynasty of Ethiopian kings to Menelik I, the son of King Solomon of ancient Israel and the Queen of Sheba. This excerpt describes Menelik I's triumphant return from Jerusalem to Aksum to become king after the people accept him as heir to the throne. As you read, notice that Menelik I is referred to as David, and his mother, the Queen of Sheba, is called Makeda.*

And the king of Ethiopia returned to his country with great joy and gladness; and marching along with their songs, and their pipes, and their wagons, like an army of heavenly beings, the Ethiopians arrived from Jerusalem at the city of Wakerom in a single day. And they sent messengers in ships to announce their arrival to Makeda, the queen of Ethiopia, and to report to her how they had found every good thing and how her son had become king, and how they had brought the heavenly Zion. And she caused all this glorious news to be spread abroad, and she made a herald to go round about in all the country that was subject unto her, ordering the people to meet her son and more particularly the heavenly Zion, the Tabernacle of the God of Israel. And they blew horns before her, and all the people of Ethiopia rejoiced, from the least to the greatest, men as well as women; and the soldiers rose up with her to meet their king. And she came to the city of the government, which is the chief city of the kingdom of Ethiopia; now in later times this city became the chief city of the Christians of Ethiopia. And in it she caused to be prepared perfumes innumerable from India, and from Balte to Galtet, and from Alsafu to Azazat, and had them brought together there. And her son came by the Azyaba road to Wakerom, and he came forth to Masas, and ascended to Bur, and arrived at the city of the government, the capital of Ethiopia, which the queen herself had built and called "Dabra Makeda," after her own name. And David the king came with great pomp unto his mother's city, and then he saw in the height the heavenly Zion sending forth light like the sun. And when the queen saw this she gave thanks unto the God of Israel, and praised Him. And she bowed low, and smote her breast, and then threw up her head and gazed into the heavens, and thanked her

> *And they blew horns before her, and all the people of Ethiopia rejoiced.*

Creator; and she clapped her hands together, and sent forth shouts of laughter from her mouth, and danced on the ground with her feet; and she adorned her whole body with joy and gladness with the fullest will of her inward mind. And what shall I say of the rejoicing which took place then in the country of Ethiopia, and of the joy of the people, both of man and beast, from the least to the greatest, and of both women and men? And pavilions and tents were placed at the foot of Dabra Makeda on the flat plain by the side of good water, and they slaughtered thirty-two thousand stalled oxen and bulls. And they set Zion upon the fortress of Dabra Makeda, and made ready for her three hundred guards who wielded swords to watch over the pavilion of Zion, together with her own men and her nobles, the mighty men of Israel. And her own guards were three hundred men who bore swords, and in addition to these her son David had seven hundred guards. And they rejoiced exceedingly with great glory and pleasure being arrayed in fine apparel, for the kingdom was directed by her from the Sea of Aleba to the Sea of Oseka, and everyone obeyed her command. And she had exceedingly great honor and riches; none before her ever had the like, and none after her shall ever have the like. In those days Solomon was king in Jerusalem, and Makeda was queen in Ethiopia. Unto both of them were given wisdom, and glory, and riches, and graciousness, and understanding, and beauty of voice (or, eloquence of speech) and intelligence. And gold and silver were held as cheaply as brass, and rich stuffs wherein gold was woven were as common as linen garments, and the cattle and the horses were innumerable. And on the third day Makeda delivered over to her son seventeen thousand and seven hundred chosen horses, which were to watch the army of the enemy, and would again plunder the cities of the enemy, and seven thousand and seven hundred mares that had borne foals, and one thousand female mules, and seven hundred chosen mules, and apparel of honor, gold and silver measured by the gomor, and measured by the kor, some six and some seven, and she delivered over to her son everything that was his by law, and all the throne of her kingdom.

And the queen said unto her nobles: "Speak ye now, and swear ye by the heavenly Zion that ye will not make women queens or set them upon the throne of the kingdom of Ethiopia, and that no one except the male seed of David [i.e., Menelik], the son of Solomon the king, shall ever reign over Ethiopia, and that ye will never make women queens." And all the nobles of the king's house swore, and the governors, and the councillors, and the administrators.

And she made Elmeyas and Azaryas (Azariah) the chief of the priests and the chief of the dea- cons, and they made the kingdom anew, and the sons of the mighty men of Israel performed the Law, together with their King David, in the Tabernacle of Witness, and the kingdom was made anew. And the hearts of the people shone at the sight of Zion, the Tabernacle of the Law of God, and the people of Ethiopia cast aside their idols, and they worshipped their Creator, the God who had made them. And the men of Ethiopia for- sook their works, and loved the righteousness and justice that God loveth. . . . They forsook divination and magic, and chose repentance and tears for God's sake. They forsook augury by means of birds and the use of omens, and they returned to hearken unto God and to make sacrifice unto Him. They forsook the pleasures of the gods who were devils, and chose the service and praise of God. The daughters of Jerusalem suffered disgrace, and the daughters of Ethiopia were held in honor; the daughter of Judah was sad, whilst the daughter of Ethiopia rejoiced; the mountains of Ethiopia rejoiced, and the mountains of Lebanon mourned. The people of Ethiopia were chosen from among idols and graven images, and the people of Israel were rejected. The daughters of Zion were reject- ed, and the daughters of Ethiopia were honored; the old men of Israel became objects of contempt, and the old men of Ethiopia were honored. For

God accepted the peoples who had been cast away and rejected Israel, for Zion was taken away from them and she came into the country of Ethiopia. For wheresoever God is pleased for her to dwell, there is her habitation, and where He is not pleased that she should dwell she dwelleth not; He is her founder, and Maker, and Builder, the Good God in the temple of His holiness, the habitation of His glory, with His Son and the Holy Spirit, forever and ever. Amen.

And Makeda, the queen of Ethiopia, gave the king- dom to her son David [i.e., Menelik], the son of Solomon, the king of Israel, and she said unto him: "Take the kingdom. I have given it unto thee. I have made king him whom God hath made king, and I have chosen him whom God hath chosen as the keeper of His Pavilion. I am well pleased with him whom God hath been pleased to make the envoy of the Tabernacle of His Covenant and His law. I have mag- nified him whom God hath magni- fied as the director of His widows, and I have honored him whom God hath honored as the giver of food to orphans."

"I have made king him whom God hath made king."

And the king rose up and girded up his apparel, and he bowed low before his moth- er, and said unto her: "Thou art the queen, O my Lady, and I will serve thee in every thing which thou commandest me, whether it be to death or whether it be to life. Wheresoever thou sendest me I will be sent, and wheresoever thou orderest me to be there will I be, and whatsoever thou command- est me to do that will I do. For thou art the head and I am the foot, and thou art the lady and I am thy slave; everything shall be performed according to thy order, and none shall transgress thy com- mandment, and I will do everything that thou wish- est. But pray for me that the God of Israel may deliver me from His wrath. For He will be wroth— according to what they tell us—if we do not make our hearts right to do His will, and if we do not readily observe all His commands in respect to Zion, the habitation of the glory of God. For the Angel of His host is with us, who directed us and brought us hither, and he shall neither depart from us nor forsake us.

"And now, hearken unto me, O my lady. If I and those who are after me behave rightly and do His will, God shall dwell with us, and shall preserve us from all evil and from the hand of our enemy. But if we do not keep our hearts right with Him He will be wroth with us, and will turn away His face from us, and will punish us, and our enemies will plunder us, and fear and trembling shall come to us from the place whence we expect them not, and they will rise up against us, and will overcome us in war, and will destroy us. On the other hand, if we do the will of God, and do what is right in respect of Zion, we shall become chosen men, and no one shall have the power to treat us evilly in the mountain of His holiness whilst His habitation is with us. "And behold, we have brought with us the whole law of the kingdom and the commandment of God, which Zadok the high priest declared unto us when he anointed me with the oil of sovereignty in the house of the sanctuary of God, the horn of oil, which is the unguent of priesthood and royalty, being in his hand. And he did unto us that which was written in the law, and we were anointed; Azariah to the priesthood and I to the kingdom, and Almeyas, the mouth of God, keeper of the law, that is to say, keeper of Zion, and the ear of the king in every path of righteousness. And they commanded me that I should do nothing except under their advice, and they set us before the king and before the elders of Israel, and all the people heard whilst Zadok the priest was giving us the commands. And the horns and the organs were blown, and the sounds of their harps and musical instruments, and the noise of their outcries which were made at that time were in the gates of Jerusalem. But what shall I tell unto you, O ye who were present there? It seemed to us that the earth quaked from her very foundations, and that the heavens above our heads thundered, and the heart trembled with the knees."

from Sir Ernest A. Wallis Budge, trans., *Kebra Negast* (London: Oxford University Press, 1932). Reprinted in Harold Courlander, *A Treasury of African Folklore* (New York: Marlowe & Company), 534–537.

Research Options

1. ***Comparing and Contrasting*** In the *Kebra Negast*, Queen Makeda travels from Aksum to visit King Solomon in Jerusalem. After returning home, she gives birth to a son, Menelik. Read the Biblical account of the meeting of King Solomon and the Queen of Sheba in I Kings 10: 2–13. Compare the two versions of the story.

2. ***Using Research in Writing*** Find out more about legends like the one in the *Kebra Negast*. What are some of the characteristics of legends? What legends are you familiar with? Write a summary of a favorite legend and recite it to your class.

CHAPTER
8
Section 1

HISTORYMAKERS **The Nok Culture**
Ancient Artists of Africa

"The truth of the matter at present is that we just do not know who the Nok peoples were or how they lived. We have no written records, we have no legends or myths that explain them."—historian E. Jefferson Murphy

In 1936, some tin miners in the central Nigerian village of Nok accidentally unearthed the head of a monkey made of baked clay. That small head was the first clue that a clever, artistic people had thrived in the area long ago. Archaeologists named the people the Nok, after the village near where these artifacts were found.

Less than ten years later, more clay figures were uncovered. A nearby town, Jemaa, revealed a finely shaped human clay head that showed great artistic ability. Nok itself offered even more objects. The two sites might never have been connected, but one worker thought the Jemaa find looked similar to the monkey head found in 1936.

More finds and further study have led to some insights about the Nok. They lived in West Africa from about 500 B.C. to about A.D. 200. Their area of settlement was about 100 miles from north to south and 300 miles east to west in the valleys of the Niger and Benue rivers.

They became the first people to make iron in West Africa around 500 B.C. Researchers have found stone hoes and shallow pottery bowls that had deeply cut patterns on the inside. Scholars conclude that the bowls were used for preparing food. The patterns provided a surface that could be used to scrape tough fibers. These clues suggest that the Nok farmed. They may have also raised cattle.

Scientists know more about Nok sculpture than other aspects of Nok life. The figures that they produced have certain traits in common. The heads of Nok figures are about one-third of the overall size of the body—much larger than in real life. Scholars think that it reflects the belief that the head was the center of the person's life force and therefore of the most importance.

Nok artists also put great attention on the head, which had more detail than other parts of the body. Eyes are usually in the shape of triangles or partial circles. In almost every head, a hole has been made for the pupil in the eye. The heads also have long noses with holes for the nostrils. Ears are often of extremely large size. While the human heads have great detail, they are generally not realistic. The use of geometric patterns gives the head a stylized or abstract look. This is not true of animal heads, which are rendered in a true-to-life way.

The heads were often made by modeling the clay. Many were also pieced together. The artist created the basic head and then added pieces of clay that represented details such as eyes, ears, or noses. The artists often decorated the head by scoring or cutting it with a pointed stick or toothed comb. Then the heads were polished after they were baked.

Still, unanswered questions remain about the Nok. The fact is that historians and archaeologists do not know who the Nok people were or how they lived. There are no written records or myths that might give an understanding of these mysterious people. The Nok sculpture and a few artifacts are the only remnants that tell the story of this ancient culture.

Questions

1. *Summarizing* How did archaeologists become aware of the existence of the Nok people?
2. *Determining Main Ideas* What made researchers conclude that the Nok practiced agriculture?
3. *Making Inferences* Why did the Nok artists make heads as they did?

CHAPTER **8**

Section 3

HISTORYMAKERS **Ezana**
Christianizing King

"Ezana, the king of Aksum, . . . the king of kings, . . . never defeated by an enemy. . . . May no enemy rise against me and may none pursue me, [and] may [this be so] by the might of the Lord of the Universe."—inscription honoring Ezana

Between A.D. 325 and 360, the kingdom of Aksum rose to the height of its power under King Ezana. He forged Aksum into a powerful trading kingdom, while also changing its religion to Christianity. Even today, this area has a large Christian population, the heritage of the change brought about by Ezana.

Located in modern Ethiopia, Aksum had several ports on the Red Sea that linked the Mediterranean world to Southwest Asia and India. It was on this sea that two young Christian boys from Tyre, in modern Lebanon, were traveling around 316. While the ship was at anchor, local people attacked it and killed the crew. The two young boys, though, had been onshore. They were thus spared death, but they became slaves to the king of Aksum—Ezana's father.

The king took the boys into his house, making Aedesius his cupbearer and Frumentius his secretary. They thrived in the palace and apparently won the favor of the royal family. The king freed them just before he died. However, his widow, the queen, asked the two Christians to stay in Aksum and serve as tutors to Ezana while the boy grew up.

When Ezana became the ruling king, the two boys finally left the country. Aedesius returned to Tyre, where he became a priest, and Frumentius traveled to Egypt to talk to an important leader of the Christian church. While in Egypt, Frumentius urged that a bishop and a priest be sent to Aksum to convert the king and his people. The archbishop in Egypt agreed—and gave Frumentius the job. Frumentius returned to Aksum and began his work. He started by converting Ezana himself. However, it took many years for Christianity to spread to large numbers of Aksumites. It eventually did, and the kingdom became a stronghold of Christianity. Today, Ethiopian Christians call Frumentius the "Father of Peace," and the ancient capital city, Aksum, is a sacred site.

However, Ezana did more than change his people's religion—he also expanded his empire. Near

Aksum was another ancient kingdom, Meröe. By the time of Ezana's rule, Meröe had become weak. Nomadic peoples called the Noba had moved into the old Meröe centers and used them to threaten Aksum's trade. Ezana struck back. He led four expeditions into the land to punish the Noba. The last was, perhaps, the most destructive. He eventually defeated them and put a stop to their damaging raids. Afterward, Ezana built a stele, or stone pillar, that described his triumph in detail:

> I pursued the fugitives twenty-three—23—days
> Slaying (some of) them and capturing others and taking booty from them, where I came; while prisoners and
> Booty were brought back by my people who marched out; while I burnt their towns, Those of masonry and those of straw, and (my people) seized their corn and their bronze and the dried meat
> And the images in their temples and destroyed the stocks of corn and cotton and (the enemy).

Another inscription describes the booty that Ezana brought back from this expedition. He returned with 3,112 head of cattle and 6,224 sheep, apparently impressing his people with the great cloud of dust made by all the livestock. Ezana ruled Aksum for many years. It became a land of peace and prosperity and of growing Christian faith.

Questions

1. **Making Inferences** Did the royal family of Aksum trust Aedesius and Frumentius? Explain.
2. **Analyzing Causes and Recognizing Effects** Why would it be important to convert the ruler of a people to a new religion?
3. **Analyzing Bias** What sources give us information about Ezana's campaign? Do such sources present any problems of reliability? Explain.

Name _____ Date _____

CONNECTIONS ACROSS TIME AND CULTURES

Migrations: Bantu and Indo-European

In this chapter, you studied migrations by looking in detail at the migration of Bantu-speaking peoples into the southern part of Africa. Chapter 3 described some early migrations of Indo-European-speaking peoples. To think about these two major migrations, answer the questions that follow.

1. Chapter 3 showed the similarity of a few words in some important Indo-European languages—English, Sanskrit, Persian, Spanish, and German. This chapter mentions that there are hundreds of Bantu languages. How do experts use language to learn about patterns of migration? _____

_____

_____

2. The Hittites—an Indo-European group that migrated into Anatolia—used their knowledge of ironworking as an advantage over the peoples they conquered. What technological advantages did Bantu-speaking peoples enjoy over the hunter-gatherer groups they met in their migration?_____

_____

_____

3. When the Hittites conquered Babylon and other cities of Mesopotamia, they borrowed and adapted ideas from the peoples they conquered. What skills or ideas did the Bantu-speaking peoples adopt as they migrated through different environments? _____

_____

_____

4. The main reason for the migration of German peoples into the Roman Empire was that the Huns were attacking German territories. What is the best explanation of the cause of the migration of Bantu-speaking peoples into southern and eastern Africa? _____

_____

_____

5. Migrations may result from many causes—environmental change, economic pressure, political issues. In your opinion, what has caused the migration of people from Europe, Africa, and Asia to the Americas since Columbus's voyages? _____

_____

_____

Name _____ Date _____

CHAPTER
8
Section 1

RETEACHING ACTIVITIES *Diverse Societies in Africa*

Determining Main Ideas

The following questions deal with the societies that developed in Africa and how they adapted to their environments. Answer them in the space provided.

1. Explain what makes Africa's environment challenging for establishing settlements.

_____

_____

2. How did hunter-gatherer societies in Africa support themselves?

_____

_____

3. How did the development of agriculture affect Africa's societies?

_____

_____

4. List three characteristics of the Nok culture in Africa.

_____

_____

Reading Comprehension

Find the name or term in the second column that best matches the description in the first column. Then write the letter of your answer in the blank.

_____ 5. extensive grassy plains that usually support agriculture in Africa		a. Nok
_____ 6. ancient city located on a tributary of the Niger River in West Africa		b. griots
_____ 7. storytellers who kept Africa's history alive through oral retellings		c. savannas
_____ 8. largest desert in the north of Africa		d. Sahara
_____ 9. a religion in which spirits are involved in regulating daily life		e. Djenné-Djeno
_____10. West Africa's earliest known culture		f. animism

Name _____   Date _____

Reading Comprehension
Write your answers in the blanks provided.

1. A permanent move of people from one country or region to another is called _____.

2. Three general categories of causes for the movement of peoples are _____,
_____, and _____.

3. An example of a political cause leading to migration is _____.

4. An example of an economic cause leading to migration is _____.

5. Factors that can force people to leave one region for another are called _____ factors.

6. Factors that lure people toward a better life in a new land are called _____ factors.

7. One positive effect of migration is _____.

8. One problem that can come as a result of migration is _____.

9. One way experts trace the patterns of migration is through _____.

10. The _____ of Africa made one of the greatest migrations in history.

11. The Bantu people are believed to have spread the technology of _____ as a result of
their migration.

12. As a result of the Bantu migrations, nearly _____ of all Africans speak a Bantu
language.

Name _____ Date _____

Summarizing

Complete the chart below by summarizing the significance of each of the people, places, events, or situations to the rise of Aksum as a trading power.

People/Places Events/Situations	Significance
1. Location of Aksum on the Horn of Africa	
2. King Solomon and the Queen of Sheba	
3. Zoskales	
4. Adulis	
5. Ezana	
6. terraced farming	
7. Pillars of Aksum	

Name _____   Date _____

CHAPTER
9
Section 1

GUIDED READING *The Earliest Americans*

A. *Determining Main Ideas* As you read about the earliest Americans, take notes to answer questions about their way of life.

The earliest Americans lived as hunters and gatherers.

1. According to most experts, when and how did the first Americans arrive in North America?	2. As large animals became extinct, how did hunters adapt to this change in their environment?

The earliest Americans began to experiment with simple methods of farming.

3. How did farming develop in what is now central Mexico?	4. What crops grew well in the tropical climate of Mexico?

Agriculture dramatically changed peoples' way of life.

5. How did farming affect where people lived?	6. How did farming affect the structure of society?

B. *Clarifying* On the back of this paper, explain how the following terms and names relate to the earliest Americans.

Beringia   **Ice Age**   **maize**

CHAPTER 9
Section 2

GUIDED READING *Early Mesoamerican Civilizations*

A. *Summarizing* As you read about early Mesoamerican civilizations, fill out the charts by writing notes that describe aspects of the Olmec and Zapotec civilizations.

Olmec	
1. Geography/Environment	
2. Urban design	
3. Economy	
4. Achievements/Legacy	

Zapotec	
5. Geography/Environment	
6. Urban design	
7. Language	
8. Achievements/Legacy	

B. *Writing Descriptive Paragraphs* On the back of this paper, write a brief paragraph to describe the city of **Monte Albán.**

Name _____ Date _____

GUIDED READING *Early Civilizations of the Andes*

A. *Comparing and Contrasting* As you read this section, fill in the chart to compare three early civilizations that developed in the Andes.

Civilization	Environment	When Flourished	Aspects of Culture
1. Chavín			
2. Nazca			
3. Moche			

B. *Synthesizing* Write a brief paragraph identifying similarities in the **Chavín, Nazca,** and **Moche** cultures.

_____

_____

_____

_____

_____

_____

Name _____ Date _____

A. *Multiple Choice* Circle the letter before the term or name that best completes
the sentence.

1. The people who built the first known civilization in the Americas were the (a) Chavín (b) Nazca
   (c) Olmec.

2. The civilization that etched more than 1,000 drawings on the plains of southeastern Peru was the
   (a) Moche (b) Zapotec (c) Nazca.

3. The land bridge that once connected the Americas to Asia is called (a) Mesoamerica (b) Beringia
   (c) Nazca.

4. The first real urban center in the Americas was (a) Monte Albán (b) Chavín (c) Moche.

5. The people who built a unique civilization that thrived from about 500 B.C. to about A.D. 600 in
   the Mexican state of Oaxaca were the (a) Nazca (b) Moche (c) Zapotec.

B. *Completion* Select the term or name that best completes the sentence.

Beringia	Mesoamerica	Maize	Ice Age
Moche	Zapotec	Chavín	Olmec

1. The area of land from central Mexico to northern Honduras where the first civilizations
   in the Americas arose is called _____.

2. The period of time between about 1.9 million to 10,000 B.C. when glaciers covered large
   portions of North America is called the last _____.

3. The first influential civilization in South America was the _____.

4. By 3400 B.C. early farmers in what is now central Mexico were growing _____,
   or corn.

5. The enormously wealthy civilization that flourished on the northern coast of Peru from about
   A.D . 100 to A.D. 700 was the _____.

C. *Writing* Write a paragraph identifying the following names and telling what they
have in common.

Chavín   Nazca   Moche

Name _____ Date _____

SKILLBUILDER PRACTICE *Distinguishing Fact from Opinion*

To identify facts, look for information such as events, dates, and statistics that can be proven to be correct. To identify opinions, look for judgments, beliefs, and feelings a writer or speaker expresses. Read the passage below about the Nazca culture. Then beside each number at the bottom of the page, write fact *if the underlined phrase with that number is a fact. Write* opinion *if the phrase is an opinion. (See Skillbuilder Handbook)*

[1] One of the most baffling enigmas of archaeology lies spread on the arid plain of the [2] Nazca region, between the Pacific coast of southern Peru and the Andean foothills. It is made up of strange [3] lines stretching across the desert as far as the eye can see, incomprehensible geometric shapes and huge . . . birds and fantastic animals, [4] looking as though they had been drawn by a giant's hand.

[5] The puzzle is made even more intriguing by the fact that often the complete figures [6] can only be seen from an altitude of above 1,000 feet. Understandably, [7] there are some people who imagine that they must have been made by unknown extra-terrestrial beings, who came to earth some thousands of years ago and made

contact with pre-Columbian peoples. . . . Unless one is prepared to close one's eyes to the facts as they are known today, [8] it is hard to imagine beings of higher intelligence traveling at the speed of light. . . .

The extraordinary dryness of the plain has protected the ancient Nazca people's [9] strange designs for at least 1,500 years; in a normal climate it is unlikely that they would have lasted until now. [10] The lines are in fact two parallel rows of pebbles, containing iron and iron oxides. Too little rain has fallen to wash the pebbles out of place down the centuries.

from *The World's Last Mysteries* (Pleasantville, New York: *Reader's Digest*, 1978), 281–282.

1. _____

2. _____

3. _____

4. _____

5. _____

6. _____

7. _____

8. _____

9. _____

10. _____

GEOGRAPHY APPLICATION: PLACE
The Mystery of Poverty Point

Directions: Read the paragraphs below and study the maps carefully. Then answer the questions that follow.

In the 1840s and 1850s, a group of settlers along the Bayou Macon River in northeast Louisiana suffered from crop failures and fever. The United States government sent supplies and aid by boat. This settlement became known as Poverty Point. Approximately 100 years later, evidence of a mysterious settlement dating back to 1500 B.C. was discovered there, and the name Poverty Point stuck to the unearthed remains.

This strange culture left behind an assortment of flint blades, tools, and dart points, but the largest artifact is the massive set of earthworks spread out along the Bayou Macon. The United States Army discovered the earthworks by airplane in 1952 when a flight over the region revealed six long lines set one inside another in an enormous semi-circle. These earthworks, though worn by time, are approximately 75 feet wide at the base, 10 feet high, and 125 feet apart from crest to crest. The length of all the ridges put together would equal nearly seven miles. One archaeologist estimates that it probably took 35-40 million fifty-pound baskets to build the earthworks. Though this culture apparently had no writing, no architecture, no agriculture, and only the crudest of tools, they constructed the most elaborate and complex set of earthworks in the Americas.

Poverty Point is believed to be a type of ceremonial center in which people from outlying areas came to participate in religious, political, or social activities. The project required a degree of centralized planning and design. Because of this, many questions remain about Poverty Point. Who were these ancient people? How could they build such a complex and formally designed project? Why did they build these earthworks?

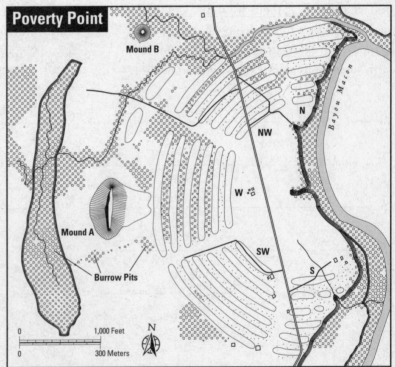

Interpreting Maps

1. How did this archaeological site get the name Poverty Point? _____

_____

2. Examine the map. Aside from the earthworks, what other remnants are evident at Poverty Point?

_____

3. How might archaeologists infer that the people at Poverty Point needed "centralized planning

   and design" to build the earthworks? _____

_____

_____

4. What might the relative location of the earthworks and river indicate? _____

_____

_____

_____

5. What is the difference in feet between the longest ridge and the shortest ridge? _____

_____

6. What are the dimensions of this site measured in feet? _____

7. Describe the layout and features of the ridges. What do you think was the purpose of these

   ridges? _____

_____

_____

CHAPTER
9

Section 1

PRIMARY SOURCE The Habitation of Monte Verde
by Lewis Lord

This magazine article reports a discovery made in February 1997 that sheds light on how long ago the Americas were inhabited. How did this new information add to what is known about the habitation of the Americas?

Scholars call them "benchmarks," discoveries that redefine much of what's known about a subject. When a finding involves the first chapter of American history—the eons before Europeans arrived—kookiness can go out the window along with scholarship. Take the issue that captivated the 19th-century academic journals: Who built the thousands of abandoned mounds that settlers came upon in the Ohio and Mississippi valleys, including one as big as the Great Pyramid of Egypt? Vikings did, some experts insisted. Other scholars credited Phoenicians, or Welshmen, or refugees from Atlantis, or the lost tribes of Israel. Some dreamed up a master race annihilated by Indian savages. Settlers liked that theory; it seemed to justify the treatment that they themselves were inflicting on the Indians. A benchmark report finally came in the 1880s. The mounds were built, the Smithsonian's Bureau of Ethnology declared, by the ancestors of a people that many Americans deemed too primitive to build anything: the Indians.

That debate ended. But others continued—like how many people lived in the New World that Columbus found. In 1939, an influential report set the hemisphere's entire population in 1492 at 8.4 million, including only 900,000 above the Rio Grande—a finding in line with Alexis de Tocqueville's cheerful claim that the Europeans settled "an empty continent." That estimate more aptly fit a later population, one that white men's diseases had reduced by 50 to 90 percent. A detailed 1966 analysis by anthropologist Henry Dobyns suggested that pre-Columbian America had between 90 million and 112 million people; by contrast, probably no more than 70 million lived in Europe.

How early? Last week, a group of archaeologists confirmed that a child's footprint found next to an ancient hearth at a site in southern Chile called Monte Verde was left 12,500 years ago. The scientists thus established a new benchmark for habitation in the Americas. Monte Verde, they agreed, is 1,300 years older than the previous standard, set in the 1930s by the finding of stone spear points near Clovis, N.M.

But in shedding light on one mystery—when did people first inhabit the Americas?—the Monte Verde scholars complicated another: How did the first Americans get here?

The earliest Americans, according to a theory supported by the Clovis discovery, came from Asia when ice covered much of North America and the seas were shallow. They crossed a land bridge between Siberia and Alaska and headed south through the Yukon, down an ice-free corridor. The land bridge and the ice-free corridor existed simultaneously about 12,000 to 14,000 years ago. That window gave the migrants 1,000 or more years to reach Clovis, a reasonable distance to cover in a millennium minus roads or wheels.

Southern Chile, however, would have been a stretch. Perhaps the ancestors of Monte Verde's settlers left Asia much sooner. Archaeologists, in fact, hope to establish that other artifacts found at the site are 33,000 years old. Or maybe the migrants moved much faster, perhaps traveling by boat along the nearby Pacific shore. Some experts doubt that the earliest Americans had such maritime skills. But who would have imagined that Indians could build Indian mounds?

Lewis Lord, "Ancient Puzzles and New Ones," *U.S. News & World Report* (February 24, 1997), 9.

Discussion Questions

Determining Main Ideas

1. How did archaeologists initially determine the approximate time period when people inhabited the Americas?

2. According to archaeologists, how long ago did people live in Monte Verde?

3. ***Analyzing Causes and Recognizing Effects*** Why did archaeologists in 1997 establish a new benchmark for habitation of the Americas?

4. ***Making Predictions*** Do you think new benchmarks for habitation in the Americas might be established in the future? Why or why not?

PRIMARY SOURCE Zapotec Urn

This stone urn—a vase with a footed base or pedestal—comes from Limatlan, Oaxaca, and represents the Zapotec god Cocijo. What details do you observe as you study the urn?

Michael Zabé/AMI/Art Resource, New York.

Research Options

1. *Using Research in Writing* Find out about the Zapotec god Cocijo. Then write a paragraph to describe what you find out and share your information with your classmates.

2. *Comparing and Contrasting* Locate pictures of stone carvings from another Mesoamerican society—the Olmec. Discuss with your classmates similarities and differences in style and craftsmanship between this Zapotec urn and one of the Olmec sculptures you find.

PRIMARY SOURCE   The Excavation of a Moche Tomb
from "Tales from a Peruvian Crypt"
by Walter Alva and Christopher B. Donnan

On February 16, 1987, looters raided the richly decorated tomb of a Moche ruler buried in the Lambayeque River valley near Sipán, Peru. Before all of the artifacts of scientific value were stolen or destroyed, Peruvian archaeologist Walter Alva directed an archaeological survey of the site. As you read an account of this survey by Alva and another participant, think about what valuable information the tomb yielded.

We began by making a contour map of the three pyramids and what remained of their ramps and adjacent plazas. The small pyramid, where the tomb had been found, was riddled with looters' tunnels, but in some places, the piles of dirt they had excavated helped preserve the original contours. The tunnels also enabled us to examine the internal construction. The pyramid and the rest of the complex evidently had been built and rebuilt over a long period of time, undergoing many changes as the various parts were enlarged. The small pyramid seems to have gone through six phases, beginning in the first century A.D. and ending about 300. Although the burial chamber had been gouged out of shape, we were able to determine that it had originally been roofed with large wood beams, which had decomposed. To our great surprise, we were able to uncover some of the tomb's contents that had been missed by the original looters and the subsequent gleaners. Clearing along one side of the chamber, we found the remains of a large, gilded copper crown decorated with metal disks; four ceramic jars modeled in the shape of human figures; and a copper mask with inlaid turquoise eyes. In excavating these, we also discovered a heavy copper scepter forty inches long, pointed at one end and bearing a three-dimensional architectural model on the other. The model depicted a platform with a balustrade, surrounding an open-front building with one back wall and a peaked roof supported by posts. Seventeen double-faced human heads decorated the roof ridge, while depicted in relief on the wall was a supernatural creature, half feline and half reptile. . . .
Knowing that the pyramid would be further plundered once we left, we decided to open up a new

section to methodical excavation, choosing a ten-by-ten-meter (1,076-square-foot) area near the summit. Here we came upon a place where the mud brick had been carved out and refilled in ancient times. Digging down, we found eight decomposed wood beams, similar to those that had roofed the looted burial chamber. Buried beneath these, in the debris of what had been a small rectangular chamber, we found 1,137 ceramic bowls, jars, and bottles. They portrayed a variety of human figures: warriors holding war clubs and shields, nude prisoners with leashlike ropes around their necks, musicians with drums, and seated figures wearing beaded pectorals (biblike coverings). Some were arranged in symbolic tableaux, for example, musicians and prisoners ringing and facing noble personages. . . .

The discoveries that subsequently emerged surpassed our dreams.

Even as these offerings were being excavated, we discovered a second, larger rectangular area that appeared to have been carved into the pyramid and refilled. As we carefully excavated this, we found, about thirteen feet below the original surface of the pyramid, the skeleton of a man wrapped in a cotton shroud. He lay stretched out on his back and wore a gilded copper helmet. Over his right forearm, which rested on his chest, was a round copper shield. A little below we found the remains of seventeen parallel beams that, we dared hope, lay over a major, undisturbed burial chamber. The discoveries that subsequently emerged surpassed our dreams. Buried in the chamber were the remains of a wood coffin that contained the richest grave offerings ever to be excavated scientifically in the Western Hemisphere. The body of a man between thirty-five and forty-five years of age had been laid to rest with a feathered headdress, banners of cloth with gilded copper decorations, beaded pectorals, nose ornaments and necklaces of gold and silver, ear ornaments of gold and turquoise, face coverings of gold, a gold backflap and a silver backflap that would have been hung from the belt, and countless other precious objects. In his right hand the deceased had held a gold and silver scepter topped with a large rattle, and in his left hand, a smaller scepter of cast silver. In relief on the rattle, which was shaped like an inverted pyramid, were scenes of an elaborately dressed warrior subjugating a vanquished opponent. The sculpted head of the smaller scepter echoed this theme. . . .

During the excavation of the warrior priest's tomb, we located another suspected tomb elsewhere on the pyramid. We held off excavation until work on the earlier find was nearly complete. The knowledge we gained made it easier to anticipate the sequence of excavation. Again we found the residue of a plank coffin containing the rich burial of a man between thirty-five and forty-five years old. Among his grave goods was a spectacular headdress ornament of gilded copper, in the form of the head and body of an owl from which arched long bands with suspended bangles, representing the feathered wings. Nearby we found the remains of four other individuals: a male between fourteen and seventeen years of age, two females in their late teens or early twenties, and an eight- to ten-year-old child. Buried with the child were a dog and a snake. . . .

The looted tomb, the two excavated tombs, and the sacrificial offerings all seem to date to about A.D. 290. While excavating the offerings, we found a fourth, somewhat earlier tomb containing the remains of a man between forty-five and fifty-five years old, also richly endowed with grave goods, including a necklace of gold beads in the form of spiders on their webs, anthropomorphic figures of a crab and a feline, scepters, an octopus pectoral

with gilded copper tentacles, and numerous other ornaments and objects. Nearby we found the body of a young, sixteen- to eighteen-year-old woman next to a sacrificed llama. This tomb may also have belonged to a warrior priest, but not all the identifying elements are there. Possibly, this is simply because it dates to an earlier period than the depictions we have of the sacrifice ceremony, which are all from after A.D. 300.

Moche civilization collapsed suddenly, probably as a result of one or more of the natural cataclysms that periodically devastate coastal Peru—earthquake, flooding, or drought. The Moche had no writing system, so they left no records we can hope to decipher. They disappeared before Europeans reached the New World and could leave us eyewitness accounts. Yet with the scientific excavation of these royal tombs, we have gained an intimate portrait of some of their most powerful words. Work at Sipán continues, now at a promising location near the tomb of the old priest. As we dig more deeply, we look forward to our next encounter.

from Walter Alva and Christopher B. Donnan, eds., *Royal Tombs of Sipán* (Los Angeles: Fowler Museum of Cultural History, University of California, 1993). Reprinted in *Natural History*, May 1994, 26–34.

Activity Options

1. *Developing Historical Perspective* With your classmates, plan a museum exhibit of some of the Moche artifacts found in the pyramid. What artifacts would you include? How would you arrange them? What would you call the exhibit?
2. *Categorizing* Make an illustration of a Moche artifact described in this article. Then work with your classmates to create a bulletin board display of recovered artifacts.

CHAPTER

9

Section 2

LITERATURE SELECTION *from* *Mexico*

by James A Michener

This novel by American author James A. Michener is set in Mexico in the 1960s. The narrator, Norman Clay, is a journalist who travels to Mexico to report on a bullfight and to learn more about his Mexican roots. In this excerpt, Clay recalls a conversation he had with his father about their Indian ancestors. As you read, be aware that Toledo is a fictional city in Mexico and that the Builders and the Altomecs are fictional peoples who are a composite of several different ancient Indian cultures.

When I was about ten years old and living once more at the Mineral, my father who, as an engineer and a scientist, was interested in speculating on historical might-have-beens, said: "At breakfast when we were talking about the choices the men sometimes have to make, you told me: 'It doesn't matter.' Well, making the proper choice can matter, Norman, and I want you to remember an excellent example of how a decision that must at the time have seemed of no consequence turned out to be vitally significant." To demonstrate this, he reached for a stick with which he drew in the sand a Y, saying:

"This will stand for a decision that had to be made about four thousand years ago by some people from eastern Asia, probably from Siberia, who crossed over the Bering Strait and hiked southward through Alaska and the western United States." (In later years I often wondered how my father could have known about this migration of our Indian ancestors, because during his time the relics of this Siberian trek had not yet been uncovered in Alaska; perhaps he was merely guessing. Of course, on one point he was quite wrong; we now know that the migrations from Asia took place not four thousand years ago but more like twenty thousand or possibly forty.)

"These Indians wandering south from Alaska came at last to San Diego," my father explained, "and they held a council to discuss what to do next. Some said, 'Let's continue down the coastline, because we've been doing that for three hundred years and it's familiar territory,' but others argued, 'Let's leave the coastline and strike out inland.' The upshot was that each group went its own way. No one could have foretold that one group had made a brilliant choice and that the other had chosen disaster."

I remember looking at the two arms of the Y and asked, "Which one did right?"

"Visualize the map of California," he said, "and think."

I tried to do this, but all I could remember was the map in my Mexican schoolbook, and it showed California merely as one of the lands stolen from Mexico by the United States, so I could not deduce the point my father was trying to make.

"Was the arm pointing to the sea the good one?" I asked.

"It led to California Baja," my father said grimly, and I instantly recalled what I had learned about that brutal, barren peninsula of heat and waterless sand. "Centuries later, when the Spaniards explored that desolate land, they found that the Indians who had gone there had degenerated close to the animal level. They lived almost without what we call a culture—no houses, not even clothing. They had no decent food and almost no water, and although the ocean about them was full of fish, they had never learned how to catch them. They were as pathetic as human beings can be and still live."

My father continued: "The other Indians chose the arm leading inland, and ultimately they reached the rich and fertile lands and, later, gold. They built three of the greatest civilizations of ancient times—the Aztecs of Mexico, the Maya of Yucatán and Guatemala and the Incas of Peru."

We stood for some minutes in silence. Then my father concluded his lecture with a statement that haunts me still, forty years after it was uttered: "You say choice means nothing? Norman, if your Indian ancestors had gone west you might now be an idiot. Thank your stars they came down through Toledo, for with the courage and the intelligence you inherited from that crowd you can become anything you wish."

Since my father's death scholars have concluded that the Indians who made the right choice reached the high valley of Toledo about twenty thousand years ago, but, as I said before, some argue it might have been as much as forty thousand years ago. At any rate, from a level thirty feet below the bottom of our pyramid, archaeologists have excavated charcoal remains that radium analysis puts at not less than five thousand years old, while along the edges of the prehistoric lake that once filled the entire valley others have dug up the skeletons of elephants killed by spears at least fifteen thousand years ago. I have spent many idle hours, on plane trips or when my eyes were too tired to read, trying to visualize these ancient Indians of the primitive period, and at times they have seemed very real to me. Fifteen thousand years before the birth of Christ they had developed some kind of civilization in the high valley. They chipped out rude spear points for hunting and carved dishes for serving food. We know little about them, but they must have feared the gods, worshipped the sun, and wondered about the accidents of death and birth. From the day of my first talks on this subject with my father I never forgot that where I lived at the Mineral, men had been living for thousands of years, and you could not say that of Richmond, Virginia or Princeton. Therefore, when in the early years of the seventh century a certain tribe of Indians gained control of the high valley, its members, some of whom we now know by name, seemed to me almost like close relatives, and when the story is told that sometime around the year 600 one of these men became leader of the tribe and began building the great pyramid, he becomes so real that he fairly shouts at me from the distant past, and the fact that the oral traditions of Toledo indicate that he was one of my ancestors gives me great pleasure.

In the year 600 the high valley looked pretty much as it does today. The last volcano had erupted some four thousand years earlier; the fantastically old lake had finally dried up; and the mountains stood exactly as they do today. In the intervening years the great piles of rock have lost possibly an inch and a half in height, due to wind erosion, but probably no more.

Far to the north, still living in caves along jungle rivers, hid the uncivilized tribes who were eventually to develop into the Altomecs and the Aztecs, but in these years they were of no consequence. To the south, living in splendid palaces decorated with silver, gold and jade, were the Mayas, whose gaudily dressed messengers sometimes reached the high valley to arrange treaties of commerce. In the valley

itself my ancestors were well established, a tribe of slim, fairly tall, dark-skinned Indians who had no real name but who were known throughout central Mexico simply as the Builders, for they had the capacity to construct finer edifices than any other peoples in the area. They knew how to quarry huge blocks of rock and transport them for miles, and they could make bricks with which to build their lesser structures.

Shortly after the year 600 a leader with a new kind of vision gained control of the tribe. He was Ixmiq, and today in Toledo a statue and a yearly festival honor his name. He had a tightly controlled personality that was ideal for exerting leadership, so for nearly fifty years he ruled unchallenged, and this gave him time to accomplish many important projects.

Waiting for an auspicious day on the calendar, he announced to his council, "I have in mind to erect a holy place for our gods ten or twenty times larger than any we have attempted before." Before his advisers could protest he added, "And we shall build it not here in the city but in a special area that shall hereafter be reserved for holy rites." He forthwith led his elders from the rude palace, which then occupied the site of today's cathedral, and took them in a northerly direction some distance from the city to where the pyramid now stands. Using piles of stones, he directed his men to lay out what seemed to them a gigantic square, but which was only about half the size of the pyramid as we now know it. His councilors protested that such a building was impossible to build, but Ixmiq insisted on its construction.

His workmen spent two years scraping away the loose earth until they reached firm earth or solid rock. He then divided the tribe into several units, which were assigned particular duties, and appointed a captain for each. Some went to live at the quarries and remained there for thirty years, passing their entire lives chipping rock. Others were the transport teams, who, with constantly increasing skill, mastered the trick of moving twenty- and thirty-ton rocks into position. Most of the men worked at the pyramid itself, inching the great blocks into position and then filling in the central portion of the structure with basketfuls of rubble, so that year by year the structure rose more impressively, and always with a flat top that grew smaller as the pyramid grew in height. These were years of peace in the high valley, nearly six centuries going by without an arrow being shot against an enemy, so that it was not imprudent for Ixmiq to assign his people to widely scattered areas and to a task that utilized the efforts of the entire community. When the huge pile had reached the intended height, it was leveled off and its spacious flat top was laid in huge blocks that took six years to work into place. Then a beautiful wooden altar was constructed so that when a priest stood at it he faced east. Four gods shared the altar and their statues lined it, with their faces turned to the west. The most important was the god of rain, for he was responsible for the flowers and the grain. Next came the sun god, the goddess of earth and a mysterious god who represented flowers, poetry, music, statesmanship and the family, and was carved in the form of a serpent with a bird's head and scales of flowers.

The pyramid of Ixmiq was a monument to peace and in the fortieth year, when it neared completion, the ceremonies that consecrated it were testimonials to peace and to one of the gentlest societies that ever existed in Mexico, or indeed, anywhere else on the American continents. The dedication ceremonies, insofar as we can reconstruct them from old carvings, consisted of prayers, dancing, the offering of hundreds of thousands of flowers, and a gigantic feast that lasted for three days. It is notable that for the first four hundred and fifty years of this pyramid's existence not a single human life was sacrificed on this altar, or lost in any other way, except for the occasional case later on when some drunken priest or reveler accidentally tumbled from its height and broke his neck.

It was a pyramid of joy and beauty, a worthy monument to the benign gods and to the farsighted man who had built it. In City-of-the-Pyramid, as the area came to be called, irrigation projects brought water from the hills down to the flat land, where flowers and vegetables were grown in abundance. Honey was collected from bees kept among the flowers, and turkeys were raised both in enclosures and in large guarded fields. Fish were available in the rivers and were kept in ponds.

The Builders dressed well in cloth made of cotton, hemp and feathers, while leaders like Ixmiq ornamented themselves with gold and silver carved with religious symbolism, which workmen also applied to some of the finest pottery ever made in the Americas. Many little statues have come down to us, representing one or another of the four major deities, and each seems to be a god whom a family could have cherished. When I was a boy we had in our home a clay figure of the earth goddess, and she was a delightful fat little woman smiling and making the land fruitful with her blessing. Whenever we looked at her we felt good, and I can think of no primitive gods that were gentler than those of Toledo. I know of few civilizations that came so close to providing an ideal life for their people. . . .

I stress these matters because throughout my adult life I have been irritated by people who glibly suppose that Spaniards brought civilization to Mexican people who had previously been barbarians, when this was clearly not the case.

In the year 600 the civilizations of Spain and Mexico were roughly comparable, except for the fact that the former had profited from the invention of the wheel, the development of the alphabet and the knowledge of how to smelt hard metals. In any event I choose to measure advances in civilization by noting such things as soundness in the organization of the state, the humaneness of the religion, the care given to the indigent, the protection of trade, the advances in sciences such as astronomy, and the cultivation of music, dancing, poetry and other arts. In these vital respects my ancestors in City-of-the-Pyramid were just about even with my ancestors in Spain and infinitely far ahead of all who shivered in caves in what would become Virginia.

Activity Options

1. *Comparing and Contrasting* With a group of classmates, analyze Michener's portrait of the Builders. Discuss which elements of their culture are similar to actual Mesoamerican cultures you have read about.

2. *Drawing Conclusions* Use a world map to trace the two routes that Norman Clay's Indian ancestors took from eastern Asia. Then estimate how many miles they migrated to their respective destinations.

Name _____ Date _____

HISTORYMAKERS The Zapotec Culture
Ancient Artists

"It was Tomb Seven which yielded the greatest returns during the first week of work at Monte Albán and proved to be one of the most important archaeological discoveries ever made in America."—archaeologist Alfonso Caso, reporting the first excavation at the Zapotec site Monte Albán

In the Oaxaca Valley in southern Mexico, the modern Zapotec people live amid the glorious creations of an earlier age. In 1932, archaeologist Alfonso Caso, desiring to learn more about the ancient Zapotec, began digging at their age-old home of Monte Albán.

Caso soon discovered several Zapotec mounds raised above the valley floor. Researchers now conclude that Monte Albán was a working city from about 600 B.C. to about A.D. 700. This time span includes three different periods of Zapotec culture.

The first period lasts from 600 B.C. to 100 B.C. and includes two important finds. The Mound of the *Danzantes* (dancers) is a pyramid that houses relief sculptures of human males in twisted shapes. At first they were thought to be dancers—thus the name of the mound. Now, researchers think that they may represent the corpses of peoples in the valley that the Zapotec conquered.

The other important find from the first period is of two stone columns, or steles. Some of the marks on these stones are the bars and dots used centuries ago in Mexico for counting. Others reflect the 260-day calendar commonly used in this area. The pillars also bear the oldest writing found in the Americas. As yet, no one has been able to understand Zapotec writing. It appears to include both symbols for sounds and symbols representing ideas. Some of the carvings show human heads upside down. Among the ancient peoples of Mexico, showing a head upside down indicates defeat or death.

The second period of Monte Albán dates from 100 B.C. to A.D. 200. It includes Mound J, an arrow-shaped platform that may have been used as an observatory. The third period is from A.D. 200 to 700. Dating from this time are spectacularly painted tombs and carved stone relief sculptures.

After this time, Monte Albán was abandoned, though researchers do not know why. Some say that local resources of wood and fertile land may have been used up. While the reason is unclear, it is certain that the town was not entirely forgotten. Though the Zapotec no longer used the site, a neighboring people apparently thought it was still a spiritually powerful place. A group called the Mixtec buried their dead in the old Zapotec tombs. In addition, the artifacts found in another Zapotec relic called Tomb Seven are of Mixtec origin. These items are made of gold, silver, turquoise, black marble, and obsidian, a glasslike rock formed by volcanoes.

Even though the Zapotec abandoned Monte Albán, they continued to live at other sites. They apparently moved their religious center to nearby Mitla. This town was farther removed from the Mixtec, who were now entering the valley. The Zapotec turned a hill near Mitla into a fortress and began expanding the town. Buildings dating after A.D. 1200 show a new stage in Zapotec art. The outside faces of these new structures included complex patterns of geometric figures made of raised stone.

These ancient sites still retain a hold on the modern Zapotec people. In his report on the first digging at Monte Albán, Caso made that clear. At the base of a stairway in Monte Albán, he found a pottery bowl with five shallow plates that had once held food. He judged the age of the pottery to be only about 50 years old. He thought the food might be a sacrifice to the ancient gods. In Mitla he found one of the ancient ruins graced with

> a wreath of flowers of the kind . . . still used by the Indians in their burial ceremonies, and the remnants of a wax candle which some pious soul had lighted to appeal to the gods of Mictlán (the realm of the dead). . . .

Questions

1. **Summarizing** What are the three periods of Monte Albán?
2. **Making Inferences** Why did the Zapotec abandon Monte Albán?
3. **Drawing Conclusions** Do the ancient Zapotec sites have any interest to the Zapotec people today? Explain.

Name _____   Date _____

CHAPTER 9
Section 3

HISTORYMAKERS **The Chavín Culture**
Uniting the Andes Peoples

"Chavín did, for the first time, join the various valley cultures in a set of common cultural practices related to religion. It therefore set the stage for later political [union] of the various valley polities into larger, inclusive empires."—anthropologists Kenneth Feder and Michael Alan Park

Two miles above sea level, in an ancient town in Peru, stands a remarkable pillar made of granite. Carved onto it is a human form with a jaw that has the sharp fangs of a great hunting cat and has snakes for hair. Called the Smiling God, the statue is thought to be the center of an ancient religion. Thousands of years ago, many different Native American peoples lived in what is now Peru. Each of these peoples developed in relative isolation. Those living on the coast had little contact with those in the high mountains nearby, and groups living in different mountain valleys had little communication. However, there is evidence of a growing cultural exchange over time. Coastal groups had long built U-shaped structures for religious ceremonies. These now began appearing in the mountains. On the other hand, mountain dwellers had for many centuries used the llama for heavy work. Llamas now began to appear in greater numbers on the coast. Around 900 B.C., the religious practices of a group of mountain people began to spread throughout the area. These people were named the Chavín after one of their chief sites, Chavín de Huantar, in central Peru. What united the people of the Chavín culture was not military conquest but religion. The Chavín religion centered on creatures that were part human and part animal. The Smiling God described above was one.

The walls of Chavín de Huantar are decorated with other versions of the Smiling God. In addition, along one side are 14 eagles that have a jaguar's fangs. They lead to another room that is home to the Staff God. This figure also has a jaguar's face and snakes for hair. He gets his name from two outstretched arms, each of which holds a long staff. Some think that the figure represents a sky god linked to the movements of the stars and planets. The Chavín also changed this temple over the years. It was enlarged, and a long walkway was added. Furthermore, the site of Chavín de Huantar shows evidence that it was a complex community in which people lived near the temples.

Chavín de Huantar was not the only temple center for this culture. Archaeologists have found other versions of the Staff God far from that site. For example, a similar figure was discovered in Bolivia, near Lake Titicaca. The people who built these other temples used the materials at hand. Chavín de Huantar was made of stone, but in the coastal areas temples were made of mud-dried brick. One site has evidence of human sacrifice. A female skeleton was buried beneath the carving of a cat's head and paws. Other locations have pyramids that include carvings of cats, snakes, and humans. Unlike Chavín de Huantar, these places do not give any indication that people lived there. They seem to be only religious sites.

The culture is revealed in more than just statues. There is also a common tradition of pottery that evolved. Many pots are decorated with cat fangs. In the early years, stoneware was either dark red, brown, or gray. Most common are open bowls and bottles; some pieces were deeply cut or scored for decorations. Later pieces are different. Bottles have longer, thinner, and more delicate spouts. Some later pieces have flower decorations. Others are made in the shape of humans, animals, or fruits. Many of the later pots are also decorated in more than one color. After 200 B.C., the Chavín culture faded. Researchers have yet to learn why. The unity brought to northern and central Peru disappeared. Now, only the stones and pieces of pottery remain to tell of their hidden past.

Questions

1. ***Drawing Conclusions*** How did geography keep the ancient Native Americans of Peru isolated from one another?
2. ***Comparing and Contrasting*** Which figure may have been more important, the Smiling God or the Staff God? Explain.
3. ***Making Inferences*** How did people in particular communities adapt the Chavín buildings to local resources?

Name _____ Date _____

CONNECTIONS ACROSS TIME AND CULTURES
Patterns of Human Settlement:
Early Civilizations

THEMATIC CONNECTION:
CULTURAL INTERACTION

As you learned in this chapter, the earliest Americans developed flourishing civilizations in Mesoamerica and in the Andes Mountains of South America. Although the rise of civilization in the Americas is relatively recent compared with the development of civilization in other parts of the world, it followed a similar pattern. To identify this pattern, complete the activities below.

1. Prospering agricultural villages and surpluses of food helped lead to the rise of civilizations. Give some examples from the rise of civilization in the Americas. _____

_____

2. According to most scholars, civilizations share five characteristics. Give examples of each of these characteristics from early civilizations in the Americas.

Advanced Cities:	
Specialized Workers:	
Record Keeping:	
Complex Institutions:	
Advanced Technology:	

3. As the economy becomes more specialized, social classes begin to emerge. Describe the social structure in Olmec culture. _____

_____

4. As populations grew, religion became more organized. Describe some religious traditions that were followed by some of the earliest American civilizations. _____

_____

5. Identify other ways in which the rise of civilization in the Americas parallels the rise of ancient civilizations in different parts of the world. _____

_____

CHAPTER 9

Section 1

SCIENCE & TECHNOLOGY *High Tech Dating Techniques*

Archaeologists use soil meters and satellite pictures to figure out where to dig and instruments such as picks and sieves to uncover artifacts. But their next task is often even more challenging—determining the age of what they find.

Scientists have developed a wide range of methods for determining the age of items discovered during archaeological digs. This process is called archaeometry and is made up of two different types of dating: relative dating and absolute dating. Relative dating gives scientists information about how old an object is as compared to other objects. For instance, bones found in a particular dig site can be dated in comparison to each other by measuring the amount of fluorine in them. Fluorine from underground water slowly seeps into buried bones. Therefore, those with large amounts of fluorine in them would be considered older than bones with small amounts of fluorine.

Absolute dating measures the age of an object in years. The absolute dating method used depends on the type of artifact being examined. Items that were alive at one time must be dated differently than objects such as stone tools.

The most common method of dating the remains of plants, animals, and humans is called radiocarbon dating. This technique determines the age of former living things by measuring the amount of carbon left behind. All living things absorb two kinds of carbon atoms from the atmosphere when they are alive: carbon 12 and carbon 14, which is known as radiocarbon. In living human beings, for example, radiocarbon is constantly decaying, but it is always being replaced by food provided by plants. However, when a human being dies, the replenishment of radiocarbon stops.

Archaeologists know that the ratio of carbon 12 to carbon 14 slowly decreases from a dead person at a uniform rate. For example, scientists know that half the radiocarbon disappears after 5,700 years. Therefore, archaeologists can accurately determine the age of a specimen by measuring the amount of carbon 12 and carbon 14 left in the remains. This method works well for organisms that have died within the past 50,000 years.

A more recent technique has been developed in which scientists use a particle accelerator to actually count individual atoms of carbon 14 and carbon 12. This method allows for accurate dating of extremely small objects that are up to 60,000 years old. Modern technology has provided archaeologists and paleontologists with a wide variety of precise tools to find, uncover, and date artifacts. Further use of satellites, computers, digital photography, and sophisticated electronic devices will continue to help archaeologists understand the past.

Questions

1. ***Determining Main Ideas*** What is the most common method of dating plants, animals, and human remains?
2. ***Clarifying*** How do archaeologists determine the dates of artifacts in relation to each other?
3. ***Drawing Conclusions*** Would the remains of a living thing have more or less carbon 14 in it after being buried for 10,000 years? Why?

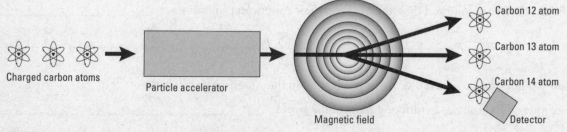

A particle accelerator shoots carbon atoms into a magnetic field. A detector then counts the carbon 14 atoms to determine the amount of radiocarbon.

Name _____   Date _____

Determining Main Ideas

Choose the word that most accurately completes each sentence below. Write that word
in the blank provided.

Tehuacan Valley	Beringia	mastodon
arts and crafts	food	maize
extinct	trading	hunting
cotton	building trades	Ice Age
sabre-tooth tiger	agriculture	

1. The ancient peoples of the Americas survived at first by _____.

2. The land bridge that connected the ancient Americas to Asia was known as _____.

3. The first people arrived in the Americas toward the end of the last _____, which lasted
    from roughly 1.6 million to about 10,000 B.C.

4. Early Americans' most challenging prey was the _____.

5. Animals that were overhunted and virtually disappeared from their habitats were thought to have
    become _____.

6. A revolution in _____, which began in central Mexico around 7000 B.C., changed the
    way of life in the Americas.

7. _____ quickly became the most important crop in the early Americas.

8. The _____, south of present-day Mexico City, was the site where several permanent
    villages were established.

9. The cultivation of crops brought about a more reliable and expanding supply of _____.

10. Improved farming eventually allowed some people to turn to non-agricultural pursuits such as
    _____ and _____.

CHAPTER
9
Section 2

RETEACHING ACTIVITIES *Early Mesoamerican Civilization*

Determining Main Ideas

Complete the following web diagrams on two early Mesoamerican civilizations. Write
your answers within each oval in the space provided.

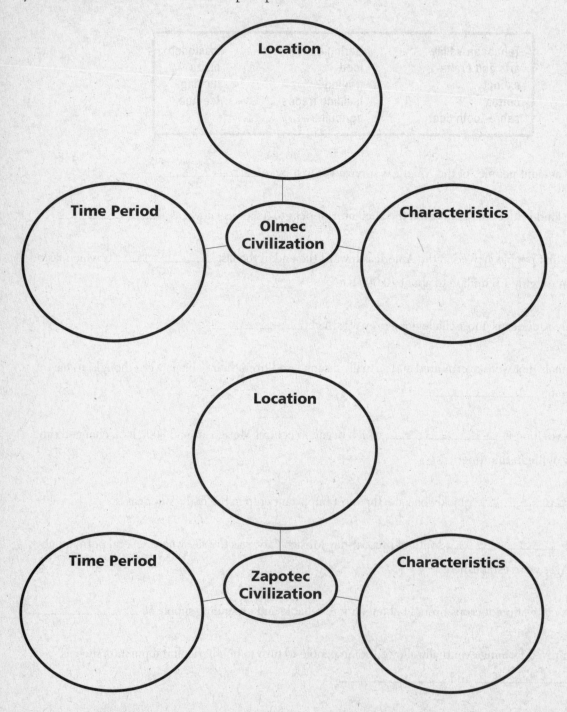

Name _____ Date _____

Multiple Choice
Choose the best answer for each item. Write the letter of your answer in the blank.

1. __ The rugged mountain range that stretches down the western edge of South America is
   a. the Rockies.
   b. the Hindu Kush.
   c. the Himalayas.
   d. the Andes.

____ 2. South America's first civilizations emerged in
   a. Brazil.
   b. Peru.
   c. Argentina.
   d. Chile.

____ 3. The first inhabitants to establish villages along the Pacific coast in South America were
   a. soldiers.
   b. traders.
   c. hunter-gatherers.
   d. farmers.

____ 4. The first important civilization that arose in the South American mountains was
   a. the Zapotec civilization.
   b. the Nok culture.
   c. the Chavín culture.
   d. the Olmec culture.

____ 5. The Nazca culture is known for its beautiful
   a. textiles and pottery.
   b. rugs.
   c. scenery.
   d. paintings.

____ 6. The unusual patterns of line drawings found on the plains of southeastern Peru belonged to the
   a. Mayan culture.
   b. Chavín culture.
   c. Moche culture.
   d. Nazca culture.

____ 7. The culture that thrived on the northern coast of Peru was the
   a. Moche culture.
   b. Chavín culture.
   c. Incan culture.
   d. Nazca culture.

____ 8. Much of the detail known about the life of the Moche comes from
   a. written records.
   b. their pottery.
   c. oral histories.
   d. cave paintings.

Answer Key

Chapter 5, Section 1
GUIDED READING

A. Possible responses:

1. provided a transportation link for the various regions of Greece; connected Greece to other societies through trade

2. made unification difficult; created independent and isolated societies

3. resulted in a small population; created a need for colonies

4. developed an outdoor life for Greek males

5. adapted and spread Minoan culture, which later formed the core of Greek religious practice, politics, and literature

6. provided basis for legend and epic, may have contributed to collapse of Mycenaean civilization

7. led to a decline in economy, trade, and writing and to a period about which we know little, since written records were not kept

B. Possible response: The history of the Trojan War was passed along through *The Iliad* and *The Odyssey*, two epic poems of Homer, a great storyteller. The Greeks developed myths about the qualities and powers of their gods to explain the mysteries of nature and human passions.

Chapter 5, Section 2
GUIDED READING

A. Possible responses:

1. made them helots, peasants forced to stay on the land they worked and turn over half their crop

2. introduced timely reforms

3. strong, highly-disciplined military state

4. outlawed debt slavery, allowed all citizens to participate in Athenian assembly

5. allowed all citizens to introduce laws, created Council of Five Hundred chosen by lot to counsel assembly

6. discipline, training, heavy armor, and the phalanx formation

7. end of Persian threat and emergence of golden age of Athens

B. Possible response: There were different ways to rule a polis, or Greek city-state: monarchy, rule by a king; aristoc-racy, rule by land-owning noble families; oligarchy, rule by a few nobles and wealthy merchants; tyrants, rule by a powerful individual; or democracy, rule by the people.

Chapter 5, Section 3
GUIDED READING

A. Possible responses:

1. increased the number of paid public officials

2. built a strong navy, expanded overseas trade, bought expensive building materials, hired artisans to create works of classical art

3. love, hate, war, betrayal, hubris

4. discussed and accepted criticism of their ideas, behavior, customs, politics

5. Society would be divided into three groups—farmers and artisans, warriors, and the ruling class. The person in the ruling class with the greatest insight and intellect would be a philosopher-king.

6. scientific method

B. Possible response: The war was an outbreak of ongoing tensions between Athens and Sparta and ended in the defeat of Athens, the loss of its empire, and the decline of democratic government.

Chapter 5, Section 4
GUIDED READING

Possible responses:

1. Goal(s): to carry out father's plan to conquer Persia

   Result(s): smashed Persian defenses at Granicus; alarmed Persian king Darius III, who raised huge army

2. Goal(s): to use surprise to overcome numerical disadvantage

   Result(s): gained control over Anatolia

3. Goal(s): to conquer entire Persian Empire

   Result(s): marched into Egypt, where he was welcomed as liberator and crowned pharaoh

4. Goal(s): to confront and destroy Persian king

   Result(s): ended Persia's power

5. Goal(s): to expand his empire eastward into India

   Result(s): won a battle against Indian army but weakened morale and exhausted troops forced a return to Babylon

B. Possible response: The orator Demosthenes urged the Greek cities to unify against King Philip II of Macedonia, who was preparing to invade Greece.

Chapter 5, Section 5
GUIDED READING

A. Possible responses:

1. Aristarchus concluded that the sun was larger than the earth and that the planets revolved around the sun; Eratosthenes used geometry to compute the earth's circumference; Ptolemy incorrectly concluded that the earth is the center of the solar system.

2. Euclid taught geometry and compiled a geometry text that is still the basis of courses in geometry; Archimedes calculated an approximate value of pi.

3. Archimedes invented the compound pulley to lift heavy objects and a device to raise water from the ground.

4. Zeno founded school of Stoicism whose ethical doctrine appealed to many different people. Epicurus founded Epicureanism, which taught that the greatest good and the highest pleasure came from virtuous conduct and absence of pain.

B. Possible response: *Hellenistic* refers to Greek culture blended with aspects of Persian, Egyptian, and Indian cultures. Located on the western edge of the Nile delta, Alexandria became a great center of trade and an international community with a diverse population. Hellenistic scholars and artists were attracted to its famous museum and library.

Chapter 5
BUILDING VOCABULARY

A. Multiple Choice

1. b

2. a

3. c

4. a

5. c

6. b

B. Completion

1. Alexander the Great

2. epic

3. tragedy

4. polis

5. Plato

6. Euclid

C. Writing

Possible Answer

The Trojan War, the Persian Wars, and the Peloponnesian War were all fought in the Mediterranean region during ancient times. According to legend, the 10-year Trojan War began in the 1200s B.C. when a Greek army attacked and destroyed Troy because a Trojan prince had kidnapped the wife of a Greek king. After the Trojan War, Mycenaean civilization collapsed. The Persian Wars, which occurred between 490 and 479 B.C., began after the Ionian Greeks revolted against Persian rule and Athens came to their aid. The Persians then attacked Athens in revenge. Several Greek city-states formed a league and defeated the Persians. Athens emerged from the victory as a powerful leader of the region. The Peloponnesian War, which lasted from 431 to 404 B.C., resulted from ill will between Athens and Sparta. Sparta attacked and defeated Athens, with the result that Athens lost all its power and its empire.

Chapter 5, Section 3
SKILLBUILDER PRACTICE

Possible responses:

1. to glorify Athens and to instill pride in its citizens for the city's heritage, which was in great danger of being destroyed

2. a. for dramatic effect and to arouse the emotions of his listeners

   b. to motivate Athenians to continue fighting to protect their lifestyle, which Pericles felt to be superior to that of their enemy

3. Pericles's goals for a strong, unified, and powerful Athens would be enhanced with victory in the Peloponnesian War. To encourage Athenians to fight on and meet these goals, he turned a funeral oration into an inspirational and patriotic speech and call to duty.

Chapter 5, Section 3
GEOGRAPHY APPLICATION

Responses may vary on the inferential questions. Sample responses are given for those.

1. the Aegean Sea, Ionian Sea, and Mediterranean Sea

2. Athens and its allies are arranged around the coast of the Aegean Sea, while Sparta and its allies are mainly arranged behind Athens with less access to the Aegean Sea.

3. Athens, because it controlled the coast—the ports and supply routes. The Spartans had no way to re-supply in the Aegean.

4. Sparta seems to have more geographic area on the map.

5. Sparta; it also has more territory on the Greek peninsula.

6. The battles raged around a peninsula named the Peloponnesus—hence the Peloponnesian War.

7. The Athenian strategy was to maintain contact with its allies and harass the Spartan coast and the arrows indicate that pattern. There are five arrows spanning out from Athens to its allies, and two others that point to areas on the Spartan coast.

Chapter 5, Section 2
PRIMARY SOURCE

The History of Herodotus

Possible responses:

1. Greeks from other city-states

2. Callimachus, Stesilaüs, Cynaegirus

3. because they formed a strong phalanx, introduced the practice of charging the enemy at a run, and fought fearlessly

Chapter 5, Section 3
PRIMARY SOURCE

Plague in Athens

1. Informally assess students' health bulletins, making sure they list symptoms of the disease in sequential order. As an alternative, you may want to have them create public service announcements to alert Athenians to the dangers of this disease.

2. Inform the guest speaker beforehand that this disease had some of the same symptoms as typhus fever. Encourage

students to ask general questions about what causes infectious diseases and how to prevent them. Students may also want to ask specific questions about such deadly diseases as the Ebola virus, SARS, or bubonic plague.

Chapter 5, Section 3
PRIMARY SOURCE

The Republic

1. Informally assess students' role-playing to make sure they understand Plato's concept of the ideal statesman.

2. Ideal qualities may include passion for knowledge, wisdom, honesty, temperance, unpretentiousness, lack of pettiness, courage, and a good memory. Students may say that Pericles, an honest, fair, and wise ruler, had many of these qualities.

3. Students' responses will vary, but they should choose world leaders who reflect some or all of the qualities discussed by Socrates and Glaucon.

Chapter 5, Section 3
PRIMARY SOURCE

Politics

Possible responses:

1. direct democracy and oligarchy

2. democracy: the free and needy majority rules; oligarchy: the rich and better born minority rules

3. Most students will say the United States is a democracy because it is government by the people, exercised through elected representatives

Chapter 5, Section 1
LITERATURE SELECTION

The Odyssey

Possible responses:

1. doubtful, suspicious, cautious, confused

2. He describes in detail how he built his bed, revealing its unique construction. Only two people—Odysseus and Penelope—know the secret of how the bed was made.

3. practical, loyal, wary, virtuous, patient, thoughtful

Chapter 5, Section 3
HISTORYMAKERS

Sophocles

Possible responses:

1. The quotation shows Sophocles's great interest in humans, which was the focus of his plays.

2. Sophocles played many different roles in Athenian life. This suggests that the Athenians thought that all citizens owed something to their city and that they needed to take time out of their work and personal lives in order to contribute to the city's life.

3. By adding another character to scenes, making the masks more expressive, and painting the scenery, Sophocles increased the human drama in his plays, which was his main interest.

Chapter 5, Section 5
HISTORYMAKERS

Archimedes

Possible responses:

1. Historians can try to determine the truth by comparing different accounts to see if they agree. They can try to identify legends by seeing when they arose; if the story first appears long after the subject's death, it is not likely to be true.

2. The lever and the pulley were Archimedes's most important inventions because they can be used in so many ways in everyday life.

3. The Roman general was angry at the soldier for disobeying his orders. The whole story suggests that people—even the enemies of Syracuse—thought highly of Archimedes.

Chapter 5, Section 3
CONNECTIONS ACROSS
TIME AND CULTURES

Possible responses:

1. a. Monarchy or tyranny, because one person has complete control of the government

   b. The Legalists might have liked Sparta's emphasis on a strong state and the citizens' dedication to keeping the state powerful. They might have disliked the rule by assembly, Council of Elders, and military kings

because the Spartan system does not give power to a single strong ruler.

2. democracy, learning, the rights of individual citizens

3. The Athenian government reacted in a similar way. Socrates was tried for corrupting Athenian youth and condemned to death.

4. a. to train citizens to be powerful soldiers

   b. Answers will vary. Some students may think education's main goal is to train people to get good jobs; others may think the main purpose is to help people learn how to solve problems or to help produce citizens who make good decisions.

5. a. insight and intellect

   b. Answers will vary. Some may think a ruler needs to be intelligent to deal with social problems and international disagreements. Others may think a ruler should be a good person to be worthy of representing the people who elect him.

Chapter 5, Section 1
RETEACHING ACTIVITIES

1. Greece is mountainous, and many small, independent communities developed. Greece also includes over 1,000 islands in the Aegean Sea. The Aegean, the Ionian Sea, and the Black Sea provided transportation routes for trade. Only a small part of the land in Greece was suitable for farming, so the country could not support much population. A moderate climate supported an outdoor life.

2. located in southern Greece on a steep ridge surrounded by a protective wall; Mycenae was main city; Mycenaeans adopted Minoan writing system and learned the value of sea travel from the Minoans; Mycenaeans fought a 10-year war against Troy (Trojan War)

3. Greeks learned their history through the spoken word, including such epics as *The Iliad* and *The Odyssey*. Greek mythology was one way people tried to make sense of the mysteries of the natural world and human behavior.

4. d

5. a

6. f

7. b

8. c

9. g

10. e

Chapter 5, Section 2
RETEACHING ACTIVITIES

1. d

2. d

3. b

4. a

5. a

6. c

7. b

8. d

9. d

10. b

Chapter 5, Section 3
RETEACHING ACTIVITIES

1. direct democracy

2. Pericles

3. Parthenon

4. classical art

5. tragedy

6. Thucydides

7. Peloponnesian War

8. philosophers

9. Sophists

10. Socrates

11. Plato

12. Aristotle

Chapter 5, Section 4
RETEACHING ACTIVITIES

1. F; Philip II was the king of Macedonia who hoped to take control of Greece.

2. T

3. T

4. F; Philip's son Alexander proclaimed himself king of Macedonia upon Philip's death.

5. T

6. T

7. F; Alexander and his exhausted forces finally turned back toward home after

winning a particularly fierce battle in India.

8. F; Alexander died at the age of 32 due to a serious illness and fever.

9. F; Three leaders took control of Alexander's empire after his death: Antigonus in Macedonia and the Greek city-states, Ptolemy in Egypt, and Seleucus in most of the old Persian Empire.

10. T

Chapter 5, Section 5
RETEACHING ACTIVITIES

1. His conquests resulted in increased trade, a shared Greek culture, and a common language that linked Egyptian Alexandria with the Asian Alexandrias in the east.

2. Greek, Egyptian, Persian, and Indian

3. Alexandria in Egypt

4. broad avenues lined with statues of Greek gods, magnificent royal palaces, Alexander's tomb, a huge lighthouse, Alexandrian library

5. that the sun was at least 300 times larger than the earth; that the earth and other planets revolve around the sun

6. that the earth's circumference was between 28,000 and 29,000 miles; modern scientists believe the earth's circumference is 24,860 miles

7. wrote the *Elements*, a collection of 465 geometry propositions and proofs, which is still the basis for geometry courses

8. accurately estimated the value of pi; explained the law of the lever

9. that people should live a virtuous life in harmony with the will of god or the natural laws that God established to run the universe; that human desires, power, and wealth should be limited; that people should focus of what they could control

10. largest known Hellenistic sculpture; bronze; stood more than 100 feet high; one of the seven wonders of the ancient world; toppled by an earthquake in about 225 B.C.

Chapter 6, Section 1
GUIDED READING

A. Possible responses:

1. Rome developed because of its location on the Italian peninsula and its fertile soil.

2. The Romans adopted their alphabet and the use of the arch, and borrowed religious ideas from them.

3. patricians and plebeians

4. became basis for later Roman law and established the principle that free citizens had right to protection of the law

5. power struggle between Rome and Carthage for control of Sicily and western Mediterranean

6. attacked Carthage, forcing Hannibal to return home

7. gave Rome domination over western Mediterranean

B. Possible response: The legislature consisted of an aristocratic Senate, with both legislative and administrative functions, and several assemblies. In the early days of the republic, the patrician-controlled Assembly of Centuries made laws. The plebeian-organized Assembly of Tribes elected representatives called tribunes to make laws, first for the common people and later for the republic. The two consuls, elected for one year each, were chief executives of the government and commanders of the army. During a crisis, the republic could appoint a dictator with absolute power for six months.

Chapter 6, Section 2
GUIDED READING

A. Possible responses:

1. agriculture, vast trading network, common coinage

2. government headed by emperor with a civil service to carry out day-to-day functions

3. discipline, strength, loyalty, practicality, usefulness

4. Slaves were numerous and important; and large differences in wealth and status separated social classes.

5. honored powerful gods and goddesses through rituals; emperor worship part of official religion

6. rich gave lavish banquets; masses

attended free games, races, and gladiator contests

B. Possible responses:

1. Caesar emerged as a leader to bring order to Rome during a period of civil war. Later, when he defied the Senate, another civil war erupted. Yet another civil war followed his assassination.

2. Julius Caesar joined forces with Crassus and Pompey to form a triumvirate that controlled Rome for ten years. A Second Triumvirate ruled Rome after Julius Caesar was assassinated.

3. Caesar's success in conquering Gaul made him popular with the Romans.

4. Appointed dictator in 44 B.C., Caesar governed as an absolute ruler.

5. leaders of the Senate who assassinated Caesar

C. Possible response: Augustus was Rome's ablest emperor; he ushered in a period of peace and prosperity called the *Pax Romana*, which lasted for about 200 years.

Chapter 6, Section 3
GUIDED READING

A. Possible answers:

1. Christianity is based on the teachings of Jesus, who emphasized God's personal relationship to each human being. Jesus's simple message attracted great crowds, particularly among the poor, and many greeted him as the Messiah.

2. Jesus was born a Jew and his teachings contained many ideas from Jewish tradition, such as monotheism and the principles of the Ten Commandments.

3. Accusing Jesus of challenging the authority of Rome, the governor had him crucified. After Jesus's death, his body disappeared from his tomb, convincing Christians that he was *Christos,* the "messiah" or "savior."

4. the first apostle; Jesus referred to him as the "rock" upon which the Christian Church would be built.

5. provided ideal conditions for travel and the exchange of ideas

6. In the Epistles and in his teachings, he stressed the universality of Christianity by declaring that the religion should welcome all converts.

7. ended persecution of the Christians in the Roman Empire and declared Christianity one of the religions approved by the emperor

8. made Christianity the empire's official religion

B. Possible response: The apostles were disciples of Jesus who spread his message. Christians gave their religion a structure with a bishop to supervise several local churches and later a pope to head the Church.

Chapter 6, Section 4
GUIDED READING

Possible responses:

1. a. raids from hostile tribes and by pirates on the Mediterranean

   b. fewer lands to conquer and resources to gain

   c. To pay off debts, government raised taxes and coined more money with less silver, which led to inflation.

   d. recruitment of foreign mercenaries; fighting among military commanders for the throne

   e. declining economic, military, and social conditions

2. doubled size of Roman armies, fixed prices to control inflation, claimed descent from Roman gods, divided empire into eastern and western parts

3. extended reforms of Diocletian, restored concept of single ruler, moved capital from Rome to Byzantium

4. worsening internal conditions, invasions by Germanic tribes and Huns, separation of western empire from wealthier eastern part

B. Possible response: Recruitment of non-Roman mercenaries caused decline of patriotism and loyalty among soldiers. The Huns, united under Attila, terrorized and plundered both halves of the empire.

Chapter 6, Section 5
GUIDED READING

A. Possible responses:

1. Greek Contributions: provided model for fine art of sculpture

   Roman Contributions: developed bas-relief, used mosaic tiles, created realistic portraits in stone, painted frescoes

2. Greek Contributions: Philosophers founded schools of philosophy, such as Stoicism, which encouraged virtue, duty, moderation, and endurance.

   Roman Contributions: applied teachings of Greek philosophers to administration of empire.

3. Greek Contributions: Provided forms and models for literary works, such as epics of Homer

   Roman Contributions: Wrote epics, as well as light, witty poetry and prose, especially history; used Roman themes and ideas in writing

B. Possible responses:

4. introduced and spread Latin, which remained the language of learning and of the Roman Catholic Church long after the Roman Empire fell

5. introduced arch, dome, and concrete; built Colosseum and other massive structures

6. built bridges, aqueducts, and extensive network of roads

C. Possible response: The poet Virgil wrote the *Aeneid*, an epic describing the history of the legendary Aeneas. Tacitus was a Roman historian recognized for his accurate presentation of the facts.

Chapter 6
BUILDING VOCABULARY

A. Matching

1. c
2. d
3. a
4. e
5. h
6. f
7. b
8. g

B. Evaluating

1. T
2. F The period of over 200 years during which the Roman Empire experienced peace and prosperity is known as the *Pax Romana*.
3. T
4. T
5. F Because the Jews rebelled against Roman rule, most of them were driven

from their homeland into exile in the Diaspora.

C. Writing

Possible Answer

In the first century B.C., Rome's government was a republic, in which citizens had the right to vote for their leaders. The government was headed by two officials called consuls, who had one-year terms and limited power. The consuls were advised by a legislative and administrative body called the senate, which had 300 members. Members of the senate were patricians, or wealthy landowners. The plebians, or lower class, could participate in the Tribal Assembly, which elected representatives called tribunes. Tribunes protected the rights of the plebians.

Chapter 6, Section 4
SKILLBUILDER PRACTICE

Possible response: The movement of the Huns from Central Asia into Europe forced the migration of Germanic tribes living north of the Danube and near the Rhine into Roman territory. These Germanic invasions brought about the collapse of the west Roman Empire.

Chapter 6, Section 2
GEOGRAPHY APPLICATION

Responses may vary on the inferential questions. Sample responses are given for those.

1. with tiny dots; a solid black line

2. about 700 miles; about 900 miles

3. The roads break for the English Channel, the southern end of the Black Sea at Byzantium, the island (modern Sicily) off the southern coast of Italy, and the western end of the Mediterranean Sea (the modern Strait of Gibraltar).

4. 53,000 miles

5. the Rhine River and the Danube River

6. They were often dangerous for citizens to travel on because bandits could attack travelers.

7. By land you could follow the northwest shoreline of the Mediterranean Sea, take ships to cross the break at the western end of the Mediterranean, and finally travel by land again to Carthage. Another way would have been to simply

travel by ships from Rome to Carthage, a mere 400 miles away over water.

8. Rome was the center of power and the road system was planned to maintain Rome's communications with all parts of its empire.

Chapter 6, Section 2
PRIMARY SOURCE

The Gallic War

Possible responses:

1. Advantages: made surprise attacks, had the ability to fight on foot, fought widely scattered rather than in a mass; Disadvantages: faced a more disciplined army, lost element of surprise because prisoners and deserters told Caesar about their defense plan

2. Advantages: were highly organized, were heavily equipped, knew where to safely cross the Thames; Disadvantages: confused by Britons' style of fighting, weighed down by heavy armor, unable to fight effectively on horseback

3. Some students may say that this excerpt shows Caesar's courage and cunning; he clearly understood what his opponents' advantages were and how to exploit their weaknesses.

Chapter 6, Section 3
PRIMARY SOURCE

Emperor Galerius' Edict of Toleration

1. Informally assess students' role-playing to make sure they understand what Galerius offered Christians in this edict.

2. Charts will vary but should include the following: Galerius offered Christians a pardon and permitted them to worship as Christians again; in return, he asked the Christians to pray to their god for the good of all Romans and the Roman Empire.

Chapter 6, Section 4
PRIMARY SOURCE

Dinner with Attila the Hun

1. Before students begin, suggest that they use props, fashion costumes, and invent dialogue to make their dramatic presentation more realistic. Then informally assess their re-creation to make sure they understand Priscus's account of the dinner.

2. Venn diagrams will vary but should indicate similarities and differences in how Attila and the other diners were dressed, where they sat, what they ate, and what tableware they used.

Chapter 6, Section 5
PRIMARY SOURCE

The Eruption of Vesuvius

1. Students will find that Roman scholar and naturalist Pliny the Elder (A.D. 23–79) wrote *Historia Naturalis;* his nephew Pliny the Younger (A.D. 62?–113?) was a Roman consul and writer whose letters provide valuable information about Roman life; and Publius Cornelius Tacitus (A.D. 55?–120?) was a Roman public official and historian whose two greatest works, Histories and Annals, concern the period from the death of Augustus to the death of Domitian.

2. Students' diagrams should indicate that the intensely violent eruption of Mount Vesuvius on August 24, an example of the so-called Plinian type of eruption, buried the cities of Pompeii and Stabiae under about 19 to 23 feet of ashes and volcanic debris and buried Herculaneum under a mud flow about 65 feet deep. Approximately 16,000 people were killed.

Chapter 6, Section 2
LITERATURE SELECTION

Julius Caesar

1. Informally assess students' interpretations of the characters. Students may prefer to perform a Reader's Theater of the excerpt.

2. Before students begin this activity, encourage them to research how Roman patricians and plebeians represented in this excerpt dressed. Then informally assess students on their sketches, making sure that they have designed costumes that accurately reflect the play's setting.

Chapter 6, Section 2
HISTORYMAKERS

Cleopatra

Possible responses:

1. Cleopatra learned the Egyptian language, which none of the other Ptolemies had ever done.

2. Rome controlled the Mediterranean world and wanted to control Egypt to gain its farmland.

3. Octavian had Caesarion killed to eliminate a possible rival for power. As Caesar's son, and possible king of Egypt, Caesarion could have challenged Octavian's rule.

Chapter 6, Section 2
HISTORYMAKERS

Julius Caesar

Possible responses:

1. Caesar won victories in Spain, he conquered Gaul, and he defeated the forces of Pompey.

2. With the riches he won in Gaul, Caesar funded popular projects in Rome. He also wrote the Commentaries as propaganda to celebrate himself.

3. Some senators simply disliked Caesar. Others feared he wished to make himself king.

Chapter 6, Section 5
CONNECTIONS ACROSS TIME AND CULTURES

Possible responses:

A. Venn diagram:
   Roman culture: 1, 2, 5, 6, 7, 8
   Both: 3
   Hellenistic culture: 2, 7, 9, 10

B. Answers will vary. Students might see Hellenistic culture as focusing more on arts, science, or philosophy, while Roman culture concentrated more on government, engineering, or law.

Chapter 6, Section 5
SCIENCE & TECHNOLOGY

Roman Construction Technology

Possible responses:

1. He wanted to build a temple to honor the Roman gods.

2. It is the huge dome that weighs over 5,000 tons and has walls 20 feet wide. It was made by pouring concrete into increasingly smaller wooden molds, one on top of the other.

3. The hole, or oculus, that was left in the ceiling gives the impression that the tem-

ple was made for the gods. It symbolized the "all-seeing eye of heaven. . . ."

Chapter 6, Section 1
RETEACHING ACTIVITIES

1. A republic is a form of government in which power rests with citizens who have the right to vote for their leaders.
2. Patricians were wealthy landowners who inherited their status and held most of the power. Plebians were the farmers, artisans, and merchants who made up most of the population.
3. Rome and Carthage fought in the Punic Wars. The end result was that Rome defeated Carthage and went on to dominate both the western and eastern halves of the Mediterranean. This ultimately led to the establishment of the Roman Empire.
4. Hannibal put together a surprise attack through the Alps on Rome that gave him free movement up and down the Italian peninsula for more than a decade.
5. b
6. e
7. f
8. a
9. c
10. d

Chapter 6, Section 2
RETEACHING ACTIVITIES

1. b
2. d
3. c
4. a
5. a
6. b
7. c
8. d

Chapter 6, Section 3
RETEACHING ACTIVITIES

1. Jew who preached, taught, and did good works; emphasized God's personal relationship to each human being and the existence of an eternal kingdom for sinners who repent; believed to be the Messiah.
2. Jesus's pupils or disciples, believed to have written some of the Gospels, the first four books of the New Testament of the Bible
3. an apostle who wrote influential letters, called Epistles, to believers; stressed that Jesus was the son of God who had died for people's sins; declared that Christianity should accept all converts, which encouraged the spread of the religion
4. Roman governor who arrested Jesus and accused him of defying the authority of Rome; sentenced Jesus to be crucified
5. Roman emperor fighting for leadership of Rome who had a vision of a cross; credited his victory to the help of the Christian God; issued the Edict of Milan, in which he declared Christianity to be an approved religion
6. an apostle who became the first bishop in Rome; called the "rock" on which the Christian Church would be built by Jesus; considered to be the first pope
7. Augustine, bishop of Hippo in North Africa, who wrote *The City of God* and taught that humans need God's grace to be saved
8. d
9. a
10. e
11. f
12. c
13. b

Chapter 6, Section 4
RETEACHING ACTIVITIES

1. *Pax Romana*
2. inflation
3. mercenaries
4. Diocletian
5. Constantine
6. Byzantium; Turkey
7. Constantinople
8. East
9. Huns
10. Attila
11. Romulus Augustulus
12. Byzantine

Chapter 6, Section 5
RETEACHING ACTIVITIES

1. the new culture produced by the mixing of elements of Greek, Hellenistic, and Roman cultures; classical civilization
2. Roman sculpture was more realistic and practical in purpose, often intended for public education.
3. a type of sculpture in which images project from a flat background; used to tell stories and to represent crowds of people, soldiers in battle, and landscapes
4. pictures or designs made by setting small pieces of stone, glass, or tile onto a surface
5. destroyed when Mount Vesuvius erupted; the burial in ash preserved buildings and works of art
6. Virgil, the *Aeneid;* Ovid, *Amores*
7. Livy and Tacitus; Livy history relied on legends and was more of a national myth of Rome. Tacitus wrote *Annals* and *Histories,* both of which present the facts accurately.
8. official language of the Roman Catholic Church into the 20th century; developed into French, Spanish, Portuguese, Italian, and Romanian; more than half the words in English have a basis in Latin
9. Roman architects created spectacular structures such as the Colosseum. They used arches for aqueducts, which brought water into cities and towns. Many large public buildings in the United States include Roman features.
10. its system of law; because it established standards of justice based on common sense and practical ideas that form the basis of legal systems in many countries around the world

Chapter 7, Section 1
GUIDED READING

A. Possible responses:

1. The government levied high taxes on farmers and taxed income from trading, mining, and manufacturing.
2. He divided the empire into provinces, each headed by a royal prince, and further divided each province into local districts, whose carefully supervised officials assessed taxes and enforced laws.

3. He waged war to expand his power.

4. He tried to treat his subjects fairly and humanely and urged religious toleration. To improve communication throughout the empire, he built extensive road systems that were pleasant for travelers to use.

5. He consolidated an empire that included Magadha and the area just to the north of it, enabling him to use the strategic central region of the Ganges River as a power base.

6. He expanded the empire with forty years of conquest. He was also a supporter of the arts.

7. His defeat of the Shakas added their west coast territory to his empire, allowing the Guptas to expand trade between India and the Mediterranean world.

8. Using diplomatic and marriage alliances, he strengthened his empire.

B. Possible response: People living in southern India spoke Tamil, and some had matriarchal societies in which the mother was head of the household. In contrast, most Indian families were patriarchal—the oldest male was head of the family.

Chapter 7, Section 2
GUIDED READING

A. Possible responses:

1. The idea that many people could become Buddhas through good works changed Buddhism from a religion emphasizing individual discipline and self-denial to one that offered salvation to all and popular worship. Buddhists became divided into two sects over the new doctrines. The new trends also inspired Indian art.

2. A trend toward monotheism developed. Although Hinduism embraced hundreds of gods, many Hindus began to devote themselves to Vishnu or Shiva. As Hinduism became more personal, it also became more appealing to the masses.

3. Writing academies were formed in the city of Madurai, and more than 2,000 Tamil poems from this period still exist. Dance and drama became popular.

4. Indians began to use a calendar based on cycles of the sun, a seven-day-week, and a day divided into hours. Scientists proved that the earth was round by observing a lunar eclipse. Numerals (including zero) and the decimal system were invented and mathematicians calculated both the value of pi and the length of a solar year to several decimal places.

5. Indian traders worked as middlemen, buying Chinese goods and selling them to traders traveling along the Silk Road to Rome. The Indians also built trading stations along the roads. The sea routes allowed Indian traders to develop or expand trade with merchants in Africa, Arabia, and China. Indians would sail to Southeast Asia to collect spices, bring the spices back to India, and sell them to Roman merchants.

6. Increased trade led to the rise of banking in India. Indian merchants who moved abroad helped spread Indian culture throughout Asia.

B. Possible response: Kalidasa, one of India's greatest writers, wrote the play *Shakuntala*. It was widely performed (and admired) throughout India. Mahayana was a sect of Buddhists who believed Buddhism should be a mass religion, offering salvation to everyone.

Chapter 7, Section 3
GUIDED READING

A. Possible responses:

1. established centralized government of top-down rule in which Liu Bang had authority over all; lowered taxes, eased harsh punishments, brought stability and peace to China

2. controlled the throne by naming one infant after another as emperor and acted as regent for each

3. conquered lands and made allies of the enemies of his enemies; set up a civil service system of training and examinations for those who wanted government careers

4. minted new money to relieve the treasury's shortage, established public granaries to feed the poor, and tried to redistribute land from the rich to the poor

B. Possible responses:

5. increased availability of books, helped spread education, promoted expansion of government bureaucracy by producing records that could be more easily read and stored

6. helped to create a worldwide demand for silk and expanded Chinese commerce all the way to Rome

7. Government recognizes need to unify the empire and promotes various methods of assimilation (e.g., intermarriage, schools to teach conquered peoples, appointing local people to government posts).

8. Political instability increases. Economic weaknesses and imbalance topple the empire.

C. Possible response: Han emperors established a centralized government in which they exercised control over the running of the empire. Government bureaucracy included civil service jobs held by civilians who had passed an examination. The government established a monopoly, exclusive control of the production and distribution of silk. To unify the empire, the Han Dynasty practiced assimilation, the process of making conquered peoples part of their culture.

Chapter 7
BUILDING VOCABULARY

A. Matching

1. h
2. c
3. a
4. d
5. f
6. b
7. g
8. e

B. Completion

1. Silk Roads
2. civil service
3. Theravada
4. Kalidasa
5. patriarchal
6. matriarchal

C. Writing

Possible Answer

In a month of traveling through India and viewing ancient art, I saw a number of stupas as well as numerous statues of Buddha and of Hindu gods. A stupa is a mound-shaped stone structure built over a sacred relic. A path encircles the stupa, and Buddhists walk the path as part of their meditation. The Hindu statues I saw depicted many gods. The three most important were Brahma, the creator of the world, Vishnu, the preserver of the world, and Shiva, the destroyer of the world.

Chapter 7, Section 3
SKILLBUILDER PRACTICE

Possible responses:

1. Emperor Asoka was so upset by the slaughter at the battle of Kalinga that he became a Buddhist and preached nonviolence and toleration.

2. Empress Lu held power in China by ruling for her young sons.

Chapter 7, Section 3
GEOGRAPHY APPLICATION

Responses may vary on the inferential questions. Sample responses are given for those.

1. The four kinds of lines refer to the four dynasties that built the sections of the wall.

2. the dates these sections were built

3. the dotted line east of Beijing leading to the sea; it is known only that it was constructed sometime during the time frame of the Ming Dynasty, A.D. 1368–1644

4. 353 B.C., 300 B.C., and 290 B.C.; 221–206 B.C.; 113–112 B.C.

5. The Han Dynasty extended the Great Wall to the west, requiring any prospective invader to circle around far to the west.

6. The Interior Great Wall is the southern-most stretch of the wall—roughly in the middle of China, within the northern bulge of the Huang He River. Sections of the Interior Great Wall are older than any other sections of the Great Wall.

7. Today's eastern-most section of the Great Wall extends almost directly from Beijing east to the Bo Hai gulf, but at one time the wall ranged hundreds of miles northeast of Beijing before dropping almost straight down to the Yellow Sea.

Chapter 7, Section 1
PRIMARY SOURCE

Arthasastra

1. Informally assess students' lists and their participation in the discussion.

2. Informally assess students' illustrations to make sure they depict one of Kautilya's security measures. Encourage students to display their illustrations.

Chapter 7, Section 2
PRIMARY SOURCE

Puranas

Possible responses:

1. someone who is obedient, fair, devout, kind, tender, humble, and sincere

2. someone who is greedy, cruel, envious, dishonest, immoral, and unkind

3. This selection focuses on Vishnu, one of the three gods that eventually became most important in Hinduism. It also concerns personal behavior more than complex rituals.

Chapter 7, Section 3
PRIMARY SOURCE

Lessons for Women

Possible responses:

1. She taught them to be humble, industrious, modest, respectful, virtuous, and clean, to continue ancestral worship, and to avoid vulgar language and gossip.

2. She might disgrace her parents, humiliate her ancestors and clan, and cause problems for her husband's family.

3. Students will likely say that these lessons would be inappropriate for American women today because they limit a woman's role to the home and emphasize woman's second-class status in society.

Chapter 7, Section 1
LITERATURE SELECTION

Panchatantra

Possible responses:

1. They wished to win the favor of kings and acquire money.

2. He had the sense to realize that the lion would kill all of them.

3. ill-considered action; because the three Brahmans did not consider the consequences of bringing a lion to life

Chapter 7, Section 2
LITERATURE SELECTION

Shakuntala

1. Before students begin, remind them that this is a comical scene. Then informally assess their performances.

2. Informally assess students' police reports. As an alternative to this activity, you may prefer to have students write a newspaper story about this incident.

Chapter 7, Section 1
HISTORYMAKERS

Chandra Gupta II

Possible responses:

1. Having a few rulers who ruled for long periods of time would help the empire have stability, which would increase the chances of peace and prosperity.

2. By taking the western regions, Chandra Gupta gained control of valuable trade. His empire may have been helped by taking the sacred city of Ujjain too.

3. Chandra Gupta changed his name and had images of himself fighting lions placed on coins to try to enhance his image as a great emperor.

Chapter 7, Section 3
HISTORYMAKERS

Wudi

Possible responses:

1. Wudi reduced the power of nobles by making them pay money to him, taking away their titles, and forcing them to break up their estates.

2. Wudi's economic policies were good for the imperial treasury in the short

term but bad for China in the long run. They weakened the economy.

3. Wudi's adoption of Confucianism as the state religion permanently influenced China, and the transmission of Chinese culture to Korea and Vietnam also had a lasting impact.

Chapter 7, Section 3
CONNECTIONS ACROSS TIME AND CULTURES

Possible responses:

1. Mauryan: highly bureaucratic organization based on Kautilya's advice

   Han: centralized government, Confucian bureaucracy

2. Mauryan: close governmental control; Asoka's policies of tolerance and nonviolence

   Han: promote assimilation of conquered peoples by encouraging colonists to intermarry with them; establish Confucian schools to train local government officials

3. Mauryan: Farmers are exempt from military service.

   Han: Farming is most honored occupation.

4. Mauryan: Asoka improves road system.

   Han: Government grants monopolies, keeps silk-making a Chinese secret, but says that commerce is the least important occupation.

5. Answers will vary. Some methods are letting immigrants become naturalized citizens, providing education, and giving protection of the laws.

6. practice tolerance and accept diversity, maintain an economic and social balance, use power wisely and fairly, promote trade and economic growth

Chapter 7, Section 1
RETEACHING ACTIVITIES

1. F; Chandragupta Maurya claimed the throne of the kingdom of Magadha in about 321 B.C., which began the Mauryan Empire.

2. T

3. F; Kautilya, one of Chadragupta's advisers, wrote a ruler's handbook called the *Arthasastra*.

4. T

5. T

6. F; Asoka's policies of toleration and nonviolence, as well as the improvements in roads made during his reign, failed to hold the empire together after his death.

7. T

8. T

9. F; India's second empire, the Magadha empire, was ruled by Chandra Gupta.

10. F; Most Indian families were patriarchal, headed by the eldest male.

Chapter 7, Section 2
RETEACHING ACTIVITIES

1. D, K
2. N
3. B
4. A
5. G
6. I
7. C
8. M
9. F, P
10. E
11. H
12. J

Chapter 7, Section 3
RETEACHING ACTIVITIES

1. a
2. c
3. d
4. c
5. b
6. a
7. b
8. d

Chapter 8, Section 1
GUIDED READING

A. Possible responses:

1. made navigation impossible to and from the coast; isolated groups who lived inland by limiting their contact

and trade with other groups living along the rivers or on the coast

2. hampered movement of peoples; mostly too hostile for people to inhabit

3. fertile land and mild climate supported large population of farmers and herders along the northern coast

4. prevented use of draft animals in farming near rain forests; also prevented invaders from colonizing fly-infested territories

5. supported abundant farming and herding that led to permanent settlements on the grassy plains, healthier lives, and increased birthrates

B. Possible responses:

6. remained hunter-gatherers; learned to identify and use resources of natural environment

7. farmed; must have mined nearby iron because they learned smelting to make iron tools for farming and iron weapons for hunting

8. fished in Niger River, raised rice and herded cattle on fertile floodplains, became prosperous through trade on Niger and overland camel routes

C. Possible response: The basic social unit was the family, which was usually an extended family that included grandparents, aunts, uncles, and cousins. Family ties often expanded into clans—groups with shared ancestry. Local religions included elements of animism, a religion in which spirits played an important role in regulating daily life. All African societies had a language, but many languages were not written down; so storytellers, such as the griots in West Africa, kept the history and culture alive.

Chapter 8, Section 2
GUIDED READING

Possible responses:

1. a. They farmed only along riverbanks.

   b. These were the only places that had enough sun.

2. a. They adapted techniques of herding goats and sheep to raising cattle.

   b. The savannas could support cattle.

3. When their farming methods or the new crops they learned to cultivate had exhausted the land, the people had to pick up and migrate to another place.

4. a. The area to the north was already densely populated and the desert was expanding southward.

 b. In territorial wars, the newcomers, with their superior weapons, drove the non-Bantu-speakers into small areas.

5. a. They exchanged ideas and inter-married with the original people.

 b. The intermingling created new cultures with unique customs and tra-ditions.

6. As a result of Bantu migrations, today there are at least 60 million people who speak one of the Bantu languages.

Chapter 8, Section 3
GUIDED READING

A. Possible responses:

1. Aksum's location and expansion made it an important trading center.

2. Merchants exchanged raw materials, goods, and ideas. Among the latter was the idea of Christianity.

3. Their land was hilly.

4. The conquest cut Aksum off from its major ports and the kingdom declined as an international trading power. The spread of Islam isolated Aksum from other Christian settlements.

5. To escape the Muslims, Aksum's lead-ers moved their capital to an isolated area over the mountains.

B. Possible responses:

Aksum: an important African kingdom that developed in what is now Ethiopia and Eritrea

Adulis: the chief seaport of Aksum

Ezana: strong leader who occupied Aksumite throne between A.D. 325 and 360

Chapter 8
BUILDING VOCABULARY

A. Multiple Choice

1. b

2. a

3. a

4. c

5. b

6. c

B. Evaluating

1. F The first West African people known to smelt iron were the Nok.

2. T

3. T

4. F A permanent move from one coun-try or region to another is called a migration.

5. F Ezana was an Aksumite king who led the kingdom of Aksum to its height.

C. Writing

Possible Answer

A huge desert, called the Sahara, stretches across northern Africa. The southern edge of the Sahara, the Sahel, is a dry region, more and more of which turns into desert each year. Most of the rest of Africa is covered by rain forests and grassy plains called savannas. Another large desert, the Kalahari, lies in southern Africa.

Chapter 8, Section 1
SKILLBUILDER PRACTICE

Possible responses:

Problem: dry climate, poor soil
Solution: practice shifting agriculture
Outcomes: exhausting soil, deforestation

Problem: need for food for herds
Solution: graze on vegetation
Outcomes: deforestation, desertification

Problem: drought and starvation
Solutions: people flee to cities; foreign aid
Outcomes: refugee camps built; food and medicine distributed; trees planted; peo-ple taught survival techniques

Chapter 8, Section 2
GEOGRAPHY APPLICATION

Responses may vary on the inferential ques-tions. Sample responses are given for those.

1. northern Africa

2. southern Africa

3. January, 10,000–7000 B.C. and July, 7000 B.C.–present

4. It falls approximately 1,500 miles fur-ther south in January, 7000 B.C.–present.

5. July and January

6. They needed water for agriculture. Also, the animals they used for survival followed the rain too.

7. As people migrate they bring their ideas, technology, language, and cus-toms with them. Migration brings about the spread of all these cultural factors.

Chapter 8, Section 1
PRIMARY SOURCE

Nok Sculpture

1. Through their research, students will find that terra cotta sculpture, from the Italian meaning "baked earth," is made of hard, semifired, waterproof reddish-brown clay that is shaped and then fired at a high temperature. You may want to invite an art teacher in your school to describe this process to the class.

2. Informally assess students' lists for information such as their appearance, their use of tools and weapons, their customs, and so forth.

Chapter 8, Section 3
PRIMARY SOURCE

Natural History

Possible responses:

1. Facts may include how far Meroë was from Napata, what flora and fauna lived there, what geographic features it had, who its ruler was, and what reli-gious beliefs its residents held.

2. Students will likely say that the infor-mation about the physical appearance of the men and animals in the region is obviously incorrect. They may draw conclusions based on what they already know about Kush in particular and on what they know about humans and ani-mals in general.

3. Students may say that spreading misin-formation might have caused ignorance, suspicion, and fear. They may say that distortions in Pliny's account, which was read by Romans and possibly by people in other parts of the world, might have squelched any plans for further explo-ration, thereby lessening opportunities for cultural exchange.

Chapter 8, Section 3
PRIMARY SOURCE

Periplus of the Erythrean Sea

1. Informally assess students' role-playing. As an alternative to this activity, have students make charts to list what goods

were traded in Adulis and where these goods came from.

2. Informally assess students' maps. After they have finished, have them calculate the approximate number of miles merchants traveled to get to Adulis from various points in the world.

Chapter 8, Section 3
PRIMARY SOURCE

A History of the Sudan

Possible responses:

1. because they attacked and killed Aksumites and interfered with Aksumite officials and messengers

2. Ezana and his troops burned and raided Kushite towns and cities, capturing prisoners and destroying property. As a result of his actions, Ezana effectively conquered the Kushites.

3. Some students will say that his actions were justified because the rebellious Noba refused to leave Aksumites alone. Others may view his actions as too extreme and harsh.

Chapter 8, Section 3
LITERATURE SELECTION

Kebra Negast

1. Hold a class discussion in which students compare the two stories. Both stories have a similar tone and style; however, the less detailed Biblical story does not mention the birth of Menelik.

2. Students will find that a legend is a story passed down orally from generation to generation and popularly believed to have a historical basis. Some legends they may be familiar with and will summarize include those about King Arthur, Robin Hood, Paul Bunyan, and Ichabod Crane in "The Legend of Sleepy Hollow" by Washington Irving.

Chapter 8, Section 1
HISTORYMAKERS

The Nok Culture

Possible responses:

1. Tin miners discovered some clay heads while digging in Nigeria in 1936. They linked these heads to some discovered years later at a town called Jemaa.

Archaeologists called the people who made these heads the Nok, the name of the town near the first site.

2. The presence of stone hoes and bowls that could have been used to process and store food suggest that the Nok practiced agriculture.

3. The Nok artists may have made heads larger than life-size because heads were thought to contain the person's life force. They may have been stylized rather than realistic to reflect cultural prohibitions against showing a living person.

Chapter 8, Section 3
HISTORYMAKERS

Ezana

Possible responses:

1. The royal family of Aksum probably trusted Aedesius and Frumentius. Ezana's father made Frumentius his secretary, and Ezana's mother made both Aedesius and Frumentius the tutors of Ezana. They would not have done so unless they had confidence in them.

2. By converting a ruler, a Christian would hope that the ruler would set an example for his or her people. Also, the successes of the ruler would become linked to the new religion, which would make converting more desirable.

3. We learn about Ezana's campaign from inscriptions. These cannot be completely believed, since what they say was probably ordered by Ezana himself. His goal may have been more to impress others than to tell the truth.

Chapter 8, Section 2
CONNECTIONS ACROSS TIME AND CULTURES

Possible responses:

1. When people migrate, they continue to use their own language. Languages gradually change over time, so the geographical range of related languages helps show the paths that migrating peoples followed.

2. The Bantu-speaking peoples knew how to make iron tools and weapons. That skill gave them a huge advantage in war over the San and BaMbuti peoples they encountered, whose weapons were made of wood and stone.

3. In rain forests, the Bantu speakers learned to plant crops on riverbanks where there was enough sunlight. On the savannas, they learned to herd cattle and cultivate new crops. They exchanged ideas and intermarried with people they encountered as they migrated.

4. The accepted explanation is that the Bantu speakers produced surplus food when they learned agriculture, which led to population increases and, eventually, a shortage of land. Because the desert was expanding from the north, they spread southwards in search of land for farming.

5. Answers will vary. Some moved because of environmental factors such as drought or depletion of resources; some moved because of economic pressures such as increasing population or famine; some because of the slave trade or to escape religious persecution; still others sought political freedoms.

Chapter 8, Section 1
RETEACHING ACTIVITIES

1. Vast deserts like the Sahara and Kalahari don't support agriculture, and dense rain forests prevent herding and harbor disease-carrying insects.

2. The men hunt for game while the women and children gather plant foods. Eventually, some of these societies learned to domesticate animals.

3. Growing their own food allowed Africans to build permanent settlements. Abundant food improved health and led to longer lives. It also enabled some people to turn to crafts such as working metal and making pottery.

4. They lived in what is now Nigeria between 500 B.C. and A.D. 200. They were the first West African people to smelt iron. Djenné-Djeno was one city of the Nok culture.

5. c

6. e

7. b

8. d

9. f

10. a

Chapter 8, Section 2
RETEACHING ACTIVITIES

1. migration

2. environmental, economic, political

3. religious or ethnic persecution, drive for power and control of more land

4. movement to cities where there are more jobs

5. push

6. pull

7. sharing of ideas and technologies, cultural blending

8. culture clashes, increasing unemployment and poverty, damage to environmental conditions

9. language

10. Bantu-speaking peoples

11. iron smelting

12. one-third

Chapter 8, Section 3
RETEACHING ACTIVITIES

1. The location was a crucial point for trade with Arab traders. Eventually, the trading settlements became more permanent colonies.

2. According to legend, the son of these two people founded the kingdom of Aksum.

3. thought to be the first king of Aksum; under his rule, Aksum increased its land holdings

4. Aksum's chief seaport, which helped it become an international trading power

5. ruler of Aksum at its height, between A.D. 325 and 360; conquered the Kushites and burned Meroë down; converted to Christianity

6. the use of step-like ridges constructed on mountain slopes for farming; improved agriculture in Aksum

7. hugh stone pillars or steles, which used a unique method to hold the stone together without mortar

Chapter 9, Section 1
GUIDED READING

A. Possible responses:

1. toward the end of the last Ice Age, by foot over a land bridge from Asia or in small boats

2. hunted smaller prey, fished, and gathered edible plants and fruits

3. People began planting and harvesting preferred edible plants from seeds.

4. maize, squashes, beans, avocados, chilies

5. With a reliable food supply, people settled in permanent villages.

6. Nonagricultural activities and skills developed, creating social classes.

B. Possible response: The buildup of glaciers during the Ice Age created a land corridor between Asia and Alaska across which the earliest Americans probably migrated. This land corridor was called Beringia. Thousands of years later, early farmers in Central Mexico learned to grow maize, or corn.

Chapter 9, Section 2
GUIDED READING

A. Possible responses:

1. located along Gulf Coast of Mexico, covered with swamps and rain forest and fertile river flood plains; hot and humid climate; abundant resources of salt and tar, clay, wood, rubber

2. combined pyramids, plazas, and giant sculptures; built thriving urban communities at sites such as San Lorenzo and La Venta

3. directed a large and prosperous trading network throughout Mesoamerica

4. jaguar motif and other art styles; pattern of urban design; concepts of ceremonial centers, ritual ball games, and a ruling class

5. located in mountainous region in southern Mexico; fertile soil and mild climate in valleys

6. planned cities with stone pyramids, temples, and palaces built around a giant plaza

7. hieroglyphic writing system

8. concept of urban planning; calendar system based on movements of the sun

B. Possible response: Monte Albán was an impressive urban center built atop a mountain; it combined the grandeur of ceremonial life with residential living space. Monumental pyramids, temples, and palaces surrounded a giant plaza paved with stones.

Chapter 9, Section 3
GUIDED READING

A. Possible responses:

1. Chavín: highland region of Peru; 900 B.C. to 200 B.C.; religious images reflected in stone carving, pottery, and textiles; religious centers featuring pyramids, plazas, and giant earthen mounds

2. Nazca: dry southern coast of Peru; 200 B.C. to A.D. 600; extensive irrigation systems, textiles and pottery with images of animals and mythological beings, Nazca Lines

3. Moche: northern coast of Peru, watered by rivers flowing from Andes; A.D. 100 to A.D. 700; irrigation systems, ceramic pottery, beautifully crafted gold and silver jewelry, musical instruments, woven clothing, tombs

B. Possible response: All three cultures successfully adapted to a harsh, rugged environment. All built flourishing civilizations known for their art styles and beautiful crafts.

Chapter 9
BUILDING VOCABULARY

A. Multiple Choice

1. c

2. c

3. b

4. a

5. c

B. Completion

1. Mesoamerica

2. Ice Age

3. Chavín

4. maize

5. Moche

C. Writing

Possible Answer

The Chavín, the Nazca, and the Moche were all early civilizations that arose in South America. The Chavín civilization flourished in northern and central Peru from about 900 B.C. to 200 B.C. The Nazca civilization flourished along the southern coast of Peru from about 200 B.C. to A.D. 600. The Moche civilization arose on the northern coast of Peru and lasted from about A.D. 100 to A.D. 700.

Chapter 9, Section 3
SKILLBUILDER PRACTICE

Possible responses:

1. opinion
2. fact
3. fact
4. opinion
5. opinion
6. fact
7. fact
8. opinion
9. opinion
10. fact

Chapter 9, Section 1
GEOGRAPHY APPLICATION

Responses may vary on the inferential questions. Sample responses are given for those.

1. It is a name given to a site where settlers in the 1840s and 1850s were rescued, and the archaeological site was given the same name.

2. There are some burrow pits, two mounds, and two strange ovals on the northwest side of the earthworks.

   There are also corridors through the earthworks.

3. The earthworks are built in a specific geometric design that required an overall plan.

4. Answers will vary. The people of Poverty Point might have needed the river as a source of food and nourishment. Also, they may have needed water for transportation.

5. The shortest is about 3,200 feet and the longest is about 5,500 feet.

6. approximately 5,000 feet x 4,500 feet

7. The ridges were built in a semicircle facing the river. There are four corridors that divide the ridges into five sections. Located

between the ridges appears to be small round objects. The ridges could have been used for seating or maybe for religious offerings.

Chapter 9, Section 1
PRIMARY SOURCE

The Habitation of Monte Verde

Possible responses:

1. from their discovery of stone spear points near Clovis, New Mexico, which are 11,200 years old

2. 12,500 years ago

3. because they found a child's footprint next to an ancient hearth in southern Chile at a site called Monte Verde; the footprint was 1,300 years older than the Clovis spear tips

4. Some students will say that new benchmarks are likely because new discoveries—like the one made at Monte Verde in 1997—will confirm even older habitation. They may cite the fact that archaeologists hope to confirm that other artifacts at Monte Verde are 33,000 years old.

Chapter 9, Section 2
PRIMARY SOURCE

Zapotec Urn

1. Through their research, students will learn that Cocijo is the Zapotec god of rain.

2. Before students begin, suggest that they also look for similarities and differences in materials and subject matter. Then informally assess students' discussions.

Chapter 9, Section 3
PRIMARY SOURCE

The Excavation of a Moche Tomb

1. Informally assess students' exhibit plans. Encourage them to extend this activity by designing informational wall plaques, catalogues, TV, radio, and print advertisements to publicize the exhibit, gift items related to the exhibit, and so forth.

2. Before students begin, tell them to use descriptive details in the selection to help them visualize what the recovered artifacts look like. Then informally

assess their illustrations and bulletin board display.

Chapter 9, Section 2
LITERATURE SELECTION

Mexico

1. Informally discuss students' analyses. They should find similarities in such aspects of culture as religion, architecture, social structure, customs, food, and clothing.

2. Students should trace routes from eastern Asia over the Bering Strait southward through Alaska. They may estimate that the first group of ancestors migrated about 11,000 miles to Baja California, and the second group migrated approximately 12,000 miles to Mexico.

Chapter 9, Section 2
HISTORYMAKERS

The Zapotec Culture

Possible responses:

1. The first was from 600 B.C. to 100 B.C.and includes the Mound of the Danzantes and two steles. The second lasts from 100 B.C. to A.D. 200 and includes Mound J. The third stretches from A.D. 200 to 700 and has painted tombs and carved relief sculptures.

2. Scientists do not really know why the Zapotec abandoned Monte Albán. Possibly, all the natural resources were used up.

3. The Zapotec people today still seem to care about the ancient sites. They sometimes leave food or ceremonial decorations for the ancient gods.

Chapter 9, Section 3
HISTORYMAKERS

The Chavín Culture

Possible responses:

1. Barriers created by mountains and mountain valleys made it difficult for groups in different areas to communicate.

2. Most students may suggest that the Staff God and the Smiling God seem equally important as they are both found in a variety of places throughout the region.

3. The adaptation of Chavín ideas in different localities is best seen in the construction of the temples. In the mountains where stone was abundant, they built with stone. In lower-lying regions where stone was scarce, they used mud-dried bricks.

Chapter 9, Section 3
CONNECTIONS ACROSS TIME AND CULTURES

Possible responses:

1. Expanding food supply encouraged population growth, establishment of large, settled communities, and development of specialized skills and creation of social classes.

2. Advanced Cities: San Lorenzo, La Venta, Monte Albán

   Specialized Workers: urban designers, craftspeople, sculptors, and traders in Olmec society; weavers, musicians, and doctors in Moche culture

   Record Keeping: Zapotec calendar system and hieroglyphic writing system

   Complex Institutions: trade network, elite ruling class, and planned ceremonial centers in Olmec society

   Advanced Technology: extensive irrigation systems in Nazca and Moche cultures

3. In Olmec society, there was a small ruling class of priests and nobles and a much larger class of peasant farmers. In addition, there were artisans and traders and probably a middle class.

4. Olmecs worshiped the jaguar spirits, prayed to varied nature gods, and practiced religion at La Venta; Zapotec built temples.

5. Like all ancient cultures, early American cultures learned to control their environment, create solutions to environmental problems, and use their resources to build thriving communities. They applied organization, cooperation, and leadership to massive building projects.

Chapter 9, Section 1
SCIENCE & TECHNOLOGY

High Tech Dating Techniques

Possible responses:

1. Radiocarbon dating is the most common way of detecting the age of former living things.

2. Scientists are able to determine relative dates of bones, for instance, by detecting the amount of fluorine in them. Fluorine seeps into bones from the ground. Older bones have higher amounts of fluorine in them than younger ones.

3. It would have less carbon 14 in it because dead things lose carbon after they have stopped living. Archaeologists are able to determine the age by how much carbon 14 is lost.

Chapter 9, Section 1
RETEACHING ACTIVITIES

1. hunting
2. Beringia
3. Ice Age
4. mastodon
5. extinct
6. agriculture
7. maize
8. Tehuacan Valley
9. food
10. arts and crafts, building trades

Chapter 9, Section 2
RETEACHING ACTIVITIES

1. emerged about 1200 B.C.; thrived 800–400 B.C.

2. along the Gulf Coast of Mexico in the modern-day states of Veracruz and Tabasco

3. built giant heads and monuments to their rulers; probably prayed to a variety of nature gods; directed a large trading network throughout Mesoamerica

4. around 1000 B.C., the main power, San José Mogote, had emerged; by 500 B.C., had developed forms of writing and a calendar

5. in the southwest, in what is now the Mexican state of Oaxaca

6. built the first real urban center in America, Monte Albán; controlled the Oaxaca Valley and surrounding region for more than a thousand years; Left a legacy of a hieroglyphic language and a calendar system based on movement of the sun

Chapter 9, Section 3
RETEACHING ACTIVITIES

1. d
2. b
3. c
4. c
5. a
6. d
7. a
8. b